11+
Maths

Numerical Reasoning Technique

WORKBOOK 7

Dr Stephen C Curran

Edited by Jackie Hurden & Jacqui Turner

This book belongs to

TUITION

Accelerated Education Publications Ltd

Contents

Chapter Twenty
MATHEMATICAL INSTRUMENTS

Mathematical Instruments include the following implements:

Rulers • **Set Squares** • **Protractors**
Compasses • **Calculators**

1. Rulers

Rulers are usually calibrated in metric and imperial units.

This side of the ruler is measured in metric units. They consist of metres, centimetres and millimetres:

10 millimetres = **1** centimetre
100 centimetres = **1** metre

Most rulers are shorter than **1** metre.

This side of the ruler is measured in inches. These inches are divided into eighths. Sometimes eighths are further sub-divided into sixteenths. There are **12** inches to **one** foot. This is a **6** inch ruler.

Note: **6** inches is approximately **15** centimetres.
12 inches is approximately **30** centimetres.

Metric measurements are used much more than imperial.

Example: Using a ruler, measure this line in centimetres, millimetres, and centimetres and millimetres.

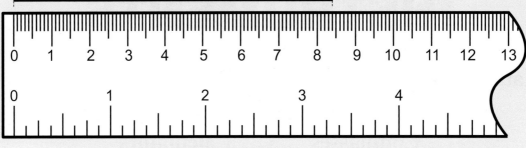

Measure this line

The measurement of this line can be expressed as:
8.4cm or **84mm** or **8cm** and **4mm**

Exercise 20: 1 Use your ruler to measure the following lines in millimetres:

1) _25_ mm

2) _62_ mm

3) _47_ mm

4) _16_ mm

Measure these lines in centimetres and millimetres:

5) _9_ cm _9_ mm

6) _3_ cm _1_ mm

Calculate the perimeters of these shapes in centimetres:

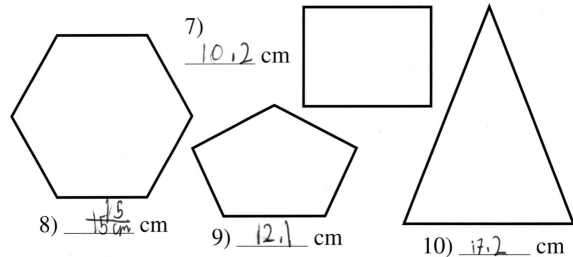

7)
_10.2_ cm

8) _15 cm_ cm

9) _12.1_ cm

10) _17.2_ cm

2. Set Squares

Set Squares are triangles made out of wood, plastic or metal. One of the angles is always a right angle. There are two types of set square:

One type has one angle of **60** degrees and one angle of **30** degrees.

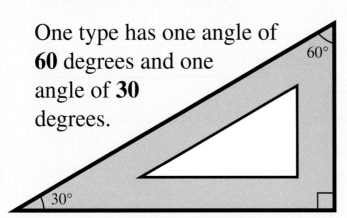

The other type has two **45** degree angles.

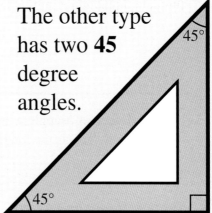

Sct squares can be used for measuring and drawing right angles and angles of **30, 60** and **45** degrees. They can also be used for drawing perpendicular lines, parallel lines and triangles or polygons with angles of **30, 60** and **45** degrees.

Example: | Indicate the various uses of set squares.

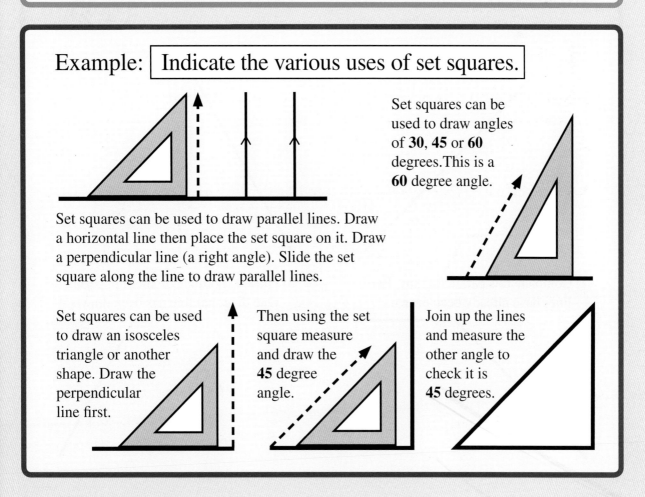

Set squares can be used to draw parallel lines. Draw a horizontal line then place the set square on it. Draw a perpendicular line (a right angle). Slide the set square along the line to draw parallel lines.

Set squares can be used to draw angles of **30**, **45** or **60** degrees. This is a **60** degree angle.

Set squares can be used to draw an isosceles triangle or another shape. Draw the perpendicular line first.

Then using the set square measure and draw the **45** degree angle.

Join up the lines and measure the other angle to check it is **45** degrees.

Exercise 20: 2

Use a ruler and set square to draw these shapes:

1) Draw a rectangle of **17cm** in perimeter.

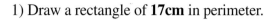

2) Complete this isosceles trapezium.

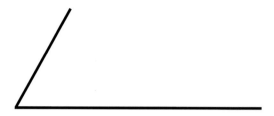

3) Draw an isosceles triangle with two **45** degree angles. This is the longest side.

4) Draw a square. The base is drawn.

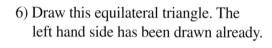

5) Draw a right angled triangle. The diagonal line has already been drawn.

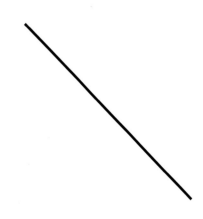

6) Draw this equilateral triangle. The left hand side has been drawn already.

7) Complete this parallelogram. Two lines have already been drawn.

8) Draw a rhombus of **16cm** in perimeter. One diagonal line has been drawn.

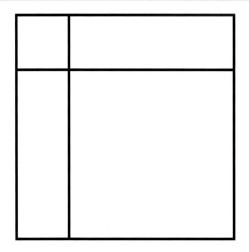

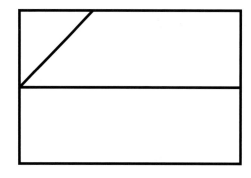

9) Complete this grid of squares by drawing in the missing horizontal and vertical parallel lines. There will be a total of **sixteen** small squares.

10) Complete this Chinese Multiplication (Napier's Bones) grid by drawing the remaining diagonal and vertical lines (see Maths Workbook 1 for examples of this type of grid).

Score ⬜

3. Protractors

A **Protractor** is used to measure the size of an angle. You can measure or draw angles to within **1°**, so it needs to be used with care. Use a sharp pencil to draw and mark angles.

This obtuse angle measures **125°**.

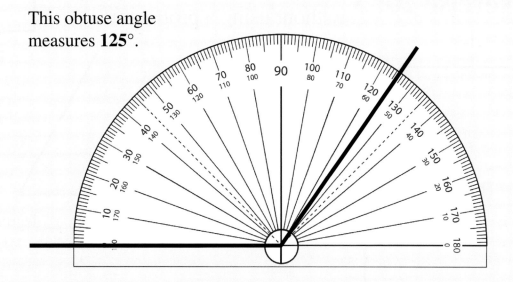

The protractor must be positioned with the **bottom edge** or **0°** on the line to be measured. The protractor has an inside and an outside scale so an angle can be measured from both sides. Make sure the angle is measured from the correct side.

Example: | Measure this angle using a protractor.

1. This angle is acute so it is less than **90°**. The base line of the angle is lined up on the **0°** horizontal line of the protractor.

2. The inside scale is used to measure the angle in an anticlockwise direction.

3. This angle measures **45°**.

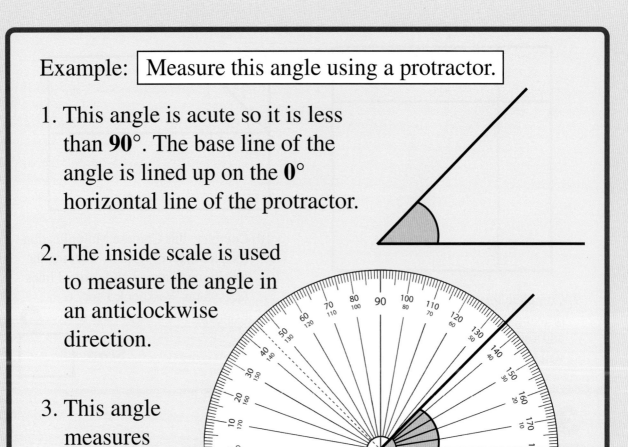

Exercise 20: 3 Estimate the size of these angles without using a protractor:

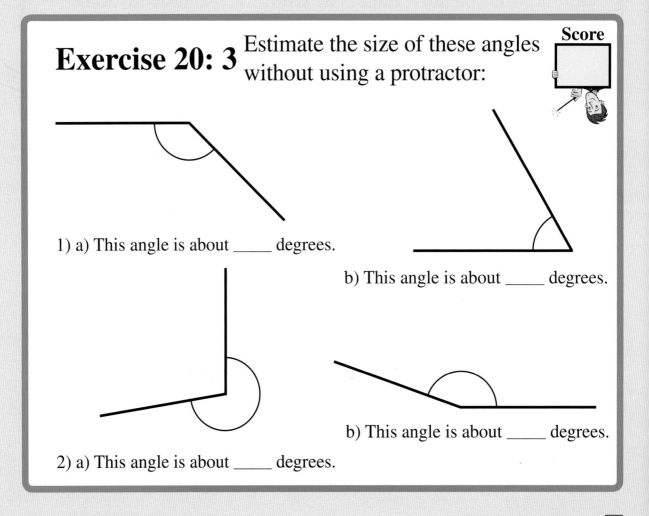

1) a) This angle is about _____ degrees.

b) This angle is about _____ degrees.

b) This angle is about _____ degrees.

2) a) This angle is about _____ degrees.

Calculate these angles using a protractor:

3) This angle is _____ degrees.

4) This angle is _____ degrees.

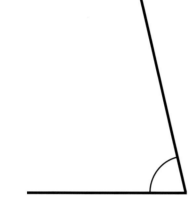

5) This angle is _____ degrees.

6) This angle is _____ degrees.

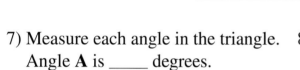

7) Measure each angle in the triangle.
Angle **A** is _____ degrees.
Angle **B** is _____ degrees.
Angle **C** is _____ degrees.

8) Draw a parallelogram using this base. With your protractor, measure the two acute angles of **40°**. The shorter sides are **3cm**.

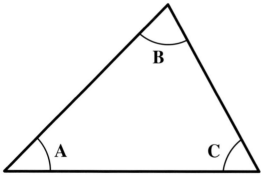

9) Draw the remainder of this kite. The equal opposite angles measure **105°**.

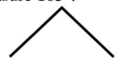

10) Measure angles **A** and **B** in this isosceles trapezium.
Angle **A** is _____ degrees.
Angle **B** is _____ degrees.

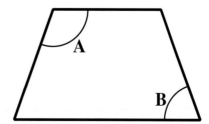

4. Compasses

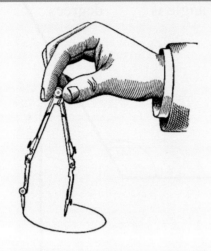

Compasses (often called a Pair of Compasses) are used for measuring equal lengths, drawing circles or parts of circles, called arcs.

Compasses are used along with rulers, set squares and protractors to draw shapes called **constructions**.

One leg of the pair of compasses ends in a sharp point and the other leg holds a lead or pencil. It is important to keep the point of the pencil or lead sharp for accurate drawing.

a. Drawing Circles

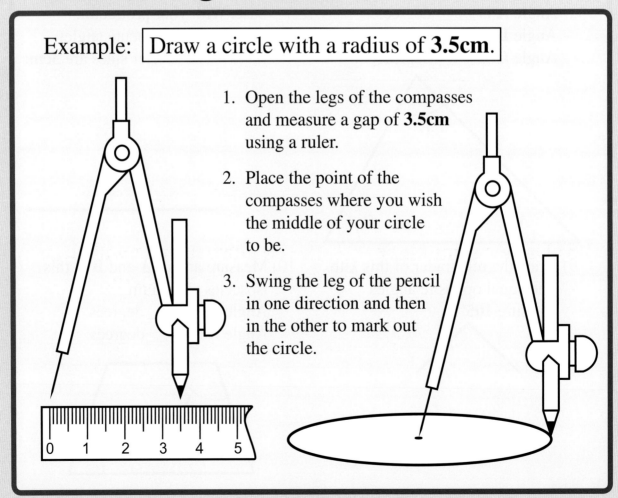

Example: | Draw a circle with a radius of **3.5cm**.

1. Open the legs of the compasses and measure a gap of **3.5cm** using a ruler.

2. Place the point of the compasses where you wish the middle of your circle to be.

3. Swing the leg of the pencil in one direction and then in the other to mark out the circle.

This circle has a
radius of **3.5cm**.

The circle has a
diameter of **7cm**.

Exercise 20: 4a Draw the following circles:

1) Draw a circle with a
   radius of **19mm**.

2) Draw a circle with a
   diameter of **5.4cm**.

3) Draw a semi-circle
   with a diameter of **6.2cm**.

4) Draw a circle with a
   radius of **2.3cm**.

b. Drawing Triangles

Example: Using a compass, construct triangle **ABC** so that **AB = 3cm; AC = 4cm; BC = 5cm**. If this triangle is constructed correctly, angle **BAC** should be a right angle (**90°**).

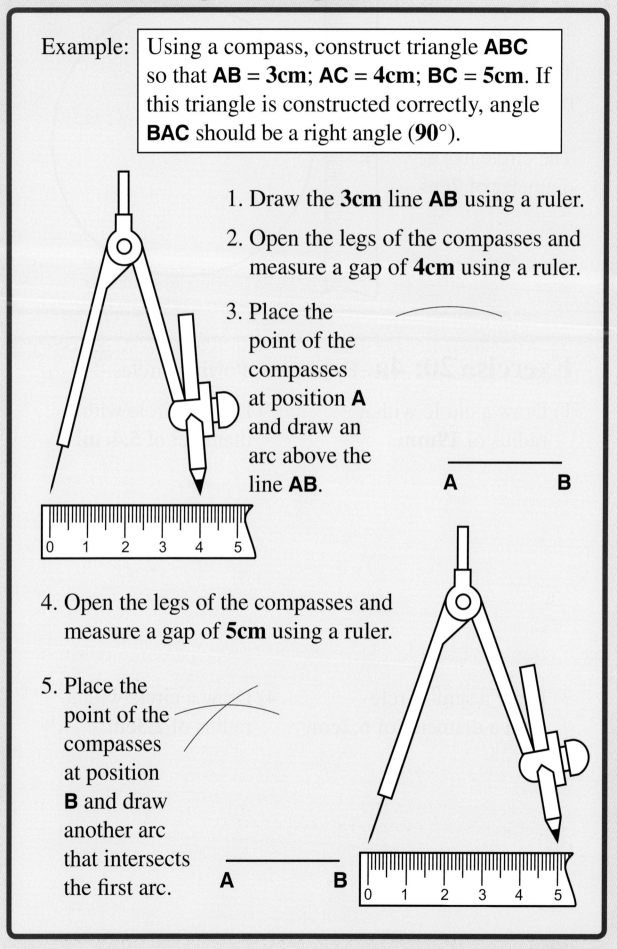

1. Draw the **3cm** line **AB** using a ruler.

2. Open the legs of the compasses and measure a gap of **4cm** using a ruler.

3. Place the point of the compasses at position **A** and draw an arc above the line **AB**.

4. Open the legs of the compasses and measure a gap of **5cm** using a ruler.

5. Place the point of the compasses at position **B** and draw another arc that intersects the first arc.

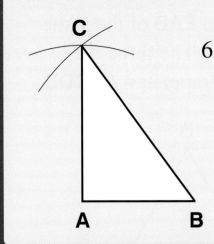

6. The triangle can now be constructed. Draw the **4cm** line **AC** and the **5cm** line **BC**. If this particular triangle is constructed correctly, angle **BAC** should be a right angle (**90°**).

Exercise 20: 4b

Construct and label the vertices of the following triangles:

5) Isosceles triangle **ABC**, **AC** and **BC** = **4.5cm**.

6) Equilateral triangle **DEF**, **DE**, **DF** and **EF** = **5.5cm**.

A ———————————————— B

D ———————————————— E

7) Scalene triangle **GHI**, **GI** = **6cm** and **HI** = **4.5cm**.

8) Isosceles triangle **JKL**, **JL** and **KL** = **52mm**.

G

H

K

J

9) Construct another equilateral triangle **EAB** of the same size that joins the other two triangles. The three triangles should make the isosceles trapezium **ABCDE**.

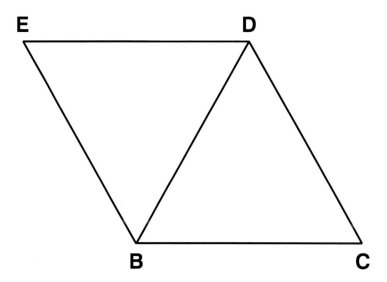

10) Construct an octagon **ABCDEFGH** by drawing six more isosceles triangles of the same size that join onto the two triangles given. Label each vertex with a letter.

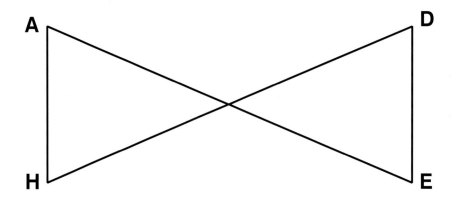

Score

© 2011 Stephen Curran

c. Bisecting an Angle

To **Bisect an Angle** means to cut it in half or divide it in two.

Example: | Create an angle bisector **YZ** from an angle **Y**.

1. Draw an angle and label it **Y**.

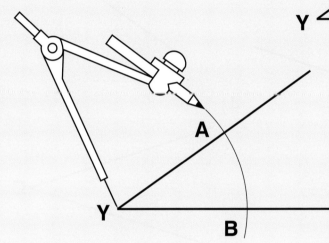

2. Put the point of the compasses on **Y**. Draw an arc cutting both lines.

3. Put the point of the compasses on **A** and draw an arc. Repeat the process at **B**. The two arcs will meet at **Z**.

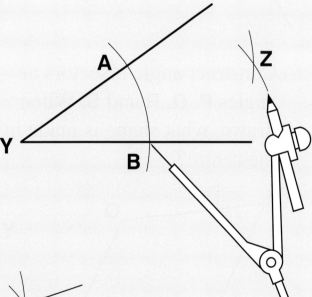

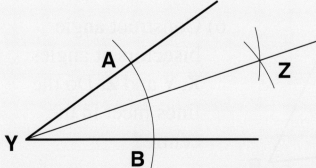

4. Join **Y** to **Z**. **YZ** is the angle bisector.

Exercise 20: 5a   Construct angle bisectors between the following angles:

1)

A

2)

B

3)

D

4)

C

5) Construct angle bisectors at angles **P**, **Q**, **R** and **S**. When drawn, what shape is made in the centre? _____

P   Q

S   R

X

Y   Z

6) Construct angle bisectors at angles **X**, **Y** and **Z**. Do the lines meet in the centre? _____

d. The Perpendicular Bisector

When a line bisects (cuts another line in half) at right angles this is called a **Perpendicular Bisector**.

Example: | Draw a horizontal line **AB**. Now construct a perpendicular bisector using compasses by drawing in the line **XY**.

1. Draw a horizontal line **AB**.

A —————————— B

2. Place the point on **A**. Open the compasses to more than half the length of the line. Now draw arcs above and below the line.

A —————————— B

3. Do not adjust your compasses. Place the point on **B**. Draw two more arcs that cut across the first two arcs.

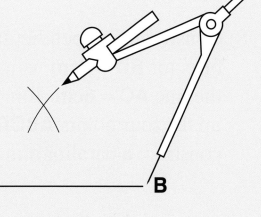

A —————————— B

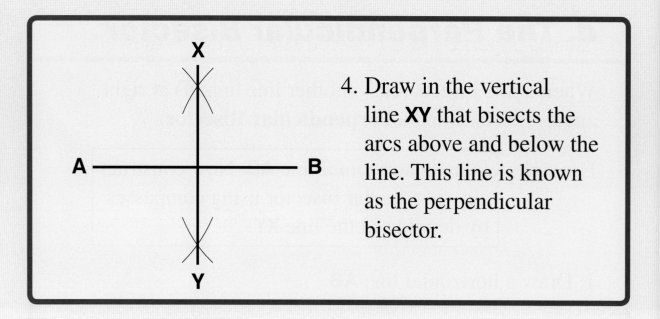

4. Draw in the vertical line **XY** that bisects the arcs above and below the line. This line is known as the perpendicular bisector.

Exercise 20: 5b Draw the following:

7) Construct a perpendicular bisector using the Line **PQ**.

P ———————————————— Q

8) Construct a perpendicular bisector **BD** = **8cm** using the line **AC** = **6cm**. Join up the four points **ABCD** to construct a parallogram.

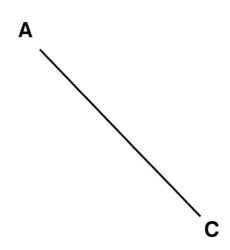

Construct perpendicular bisectors using these lines.

9)

10)

N

X ————————— Y

O

Score

5. Calculators

Standard Calculators perform a limited range of operations. They are useful tools but should not replace the need for good mental arithmetic and a sound knowledge of times tables.

The Calculator Buttons:

C Clear or Cancel.

CE Clear or Cancel the last entry.

+/– Change to Positive or a Negative Number.

MRC Memory Recall. The first press recalls contents and the second press clears the Memory.

M– Subtracts whatever is on the display from the current contents held in the Memory.

M+ Add to Memory.

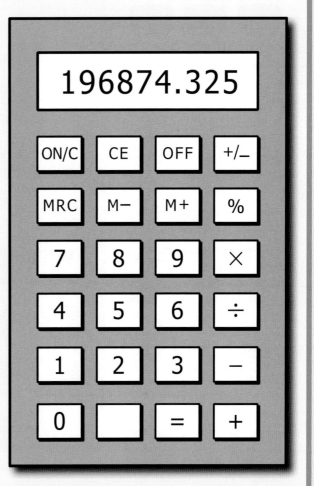

Scientific Calculators are a very useful tool. The relevant calculator buttons for general calculations are shown below:

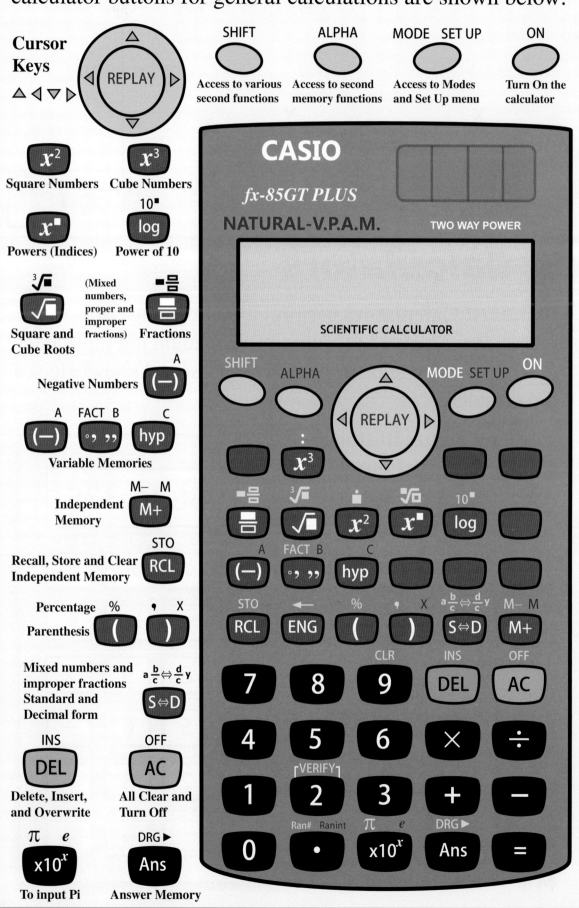

Cursor Keys
△ ◁ ▽ ▷

SHIFT — Access to various second functions

ALPHA — Access to second memory functions

MODE SET UP — Access to Modes and Set Up menu

ON — Turn On the calculator

x^2 **Square Numbers**

x^3 **Cube Numbers**

$x^{\blacksquare}$ **Powers (Indices)**

$10^{\blacksquare}$ log **Power of 10**

$\sqrt[3]{}$ $\sqrt{}$ **Square and Cube Roots**

(Mixed numbers, proper and improper fractions) **Fractions**

Negative Numbers (−) A

Variable Memories (−) A ° ' '' FACT B hyp C

Independent Memory M+ M− M

Recall, Store and Clear Independent Memory RCL STO

Percentage % **Parenthesis** ( ) ' X

Mixed numbers and improper fractions Standard and Decimal form $a\frac{b}{c} \Leftrightarrow \frac{d}{c}y$ S⇔D

Delete, Insert, and Overwrite DEL INS

All Clear and Turn Off AC OFF

To input Pi x10^{-x} π e

Answer Memory Ans DRG ▶

CASIO

fx-85GT PLUS

NATURAL-V.P.A.M.

TWO WAY POWER

SCIENTIFIC CALCULATOR

a. Getting Started

(i) Turning the Calculator On and Off

Example: Show how to turn the calculator on and off.

Step 1:   Press ⬭(ON) to turn the calculator **on**.

Step 2:   Press ⬭(SHIFT) 〔AC〕(OFF) to turn the calculator **off**.

(ii) Adjusting the Display Contrast

Example: Demonstrate how to adjust the display contrast to light or dark.

Step 1:   Press ⬭(SHIFT) ⬭(MODE SET UP) to display the first screen.

1: Mth10	2: Line10
3: Deg	4: Rad
5: Gra	6: Fix
7: Sci	8: Norm

Step 2:   Press ▽ to display the second screen.

1: ab/c	2: d/c
3: STAT	4: Rdec
5: Disp	6: ◀CONT▶

Step 3:   Press **6** to **CONTRAST** screen.

```
CONTRAST

LIGHT              DARK
[ ◄ ]              [ ► ]
```

Step 4: Press ◄ for a **LIGHT** ► for a **DARK** screen.

(iii) The Calculator Default (COMP) Mode

The calculator has three different operational modes:

- **COMP**   for general calculations (default mode)
- **STAT**   for statistical and regression calculations
- **TABLE** for generation of a table based on an expression

For the purposes of this workbook we will only be operating the calculator in the default or **COMP** mode for general calculations. This mode automatically sets the calculator to **math format**. This means calculations can be inputted and displayed in exactly the same way in which they are written.

(iv) Setting the Calculator to COMP Mode

The calculator can easily be reset to **COMP** mode if it has been changed to another mode.

Example: Show how to set the calculator to **COMP** mode.

Step 1: Press MODE SET UP ◯ to display the mode menu.

```
1: COMP        2: STAT
3: TABLE       4: VERIF
```

Step 2: Press **1** to set the calculator to **COMP** mode.

(v) Clearing the Contents of the Calculator

Another simple procedure will reset the calculator back to its factory (default) settings and clear any calculations in the calculator. It also restores the calculator to **COMP** mode.

Example: | Demonstrate how to reset the calculator. |

To reset the calculator press these five buttons in order.

1.	2.	3.	4.	5.
SHIFT	CLR			OFF
◯	**9**	**3**	**=**	AC

b. Basic Number

(i) Four Rules of Number

The $+ - \times \div$ keys are used to perform arithmetic calculations.

The calculator automatically judges the calculation priority by applying the BIDMAS or BODMAS rules.

Example 1: | Calculate $7 \times 8 - 4 \times 5$ by keying in the information in the order it is given. |

Step 1: Key in the calculation exactly as it appears.

Press

The calculator displays the calculation exactly as written.

```
7 × 8 − 4 × 5
```

Step 2: Press for the answer of **36**.

```
7 × 8 − 4 × 5

                36
```

If a mistake is made whilst inputting a character or function it is possible to make changes in the following way:

Example 2: | Change **360 × 13** to **360 ÷ 15** |

360 × 13| ← The cursor will flash.   Press [DEL] to delete the **3**.

360 × 1| ← The cursor has moved.   Press [5] to input the **5**.

360 × 15| Press [◁][◁]   to move the cursor **2** places to the left.

360 ×|15   Press [DEL] to delete the ×.

360|15   Press [÷] to input the ÷.

The sum now reads correctly as: **360 ÷ 15**

Exercise 20: 6a   Answer using a calculator:

1) $558 \div 6 - 28 \times 3 = $ _____   2) $72 \div 4 \div 12 \times 8 = $ _____

3) $20 + 6 \times 9 \div 2 = $ _____   4) $85 \times 8 \div 4 \times 7 = $ _____

5) $82 - 37 \times 3 + 680 \div 5 = $ _____

(ii) Positive and Negative Numbers

If a sum with negative numbers is inputted, the calculator automatically applies the **Positive and Negative Number** rules.

Example 2: | Calculate **-8 × -7 + 9 × -5** by keying in the sum in the order in which it is given. |

Step 1:   Key in the calculation exactly as it appears.

Press   [−] [8] [×] [−] [7]
        [+] [9] [×] [−] [5]

The calculator displays the calculation exactly as written.

$$\text{-}8 \times \text{-}7 + 9 \times \text{-}5$$

Step 2: Press for the answer of **11**.

$$\text{-}8 \times \text{-}7 + 9 \times \text{-}5$$
$$11$$

Replay Function

It is possible to change the calculation on the display after it has been executed by using the replay function.

Press then press or to edit the expression.

Exercise 20: 6b   Answer using a Calculator:

6) $\text{-}4 \times 7 + \text{-}6 - 3 =$ _____   7) $8 \div \text{-}4 \div 3 \times \text{-}6 =$ _____

8) $76 - \text{-}6 \times 21 + 51 =$ _____   9) $49 \times \text{-}39 \div 18 \times \text{-}6 =$ _____

10) $704 \div \text{-}32 \times \text{-}88 - 70 \times 68 =$ _____   **Score**

(iii) Inputting a Calculation with Parentheses

The calculator allows you to **Input Parentheses** (brackets) just as they are written. The multiplication sign can be omitted when writing $2 \times (5 + 4)$. It can simply be written in correct mathematical notation as $2(5 + 4)$ without the $\times$ sign.

Example: | Calculate $2(5 + 4) - 2 \times \text{-}3$ by keying in the sum in the order in which it is given.

Step 1: Key in the calculation exactly as it appears.

Press **2** **(** **5** **+** **4** **)** **−** **2** **×** **−** **3**

$$2(5 + 4) - 2 \times \text{-}3$$

Step 2: Press **=** for the answer of **24**.

$$2(5 + 4) - 2 \times \text{-}3$$

$$24$$

Exercise 20: 7a   Answer using a Calculator:

1) $7(\text{-}18 - 6) \times \text{-}3 = $ _____

2) $16 \div \text{-}4 + 3(\text{-}6 \times 8) = $ _____

3) $\text{-}4(6 - \text{-}3) \times 11 = $ _____

4) $52 \times \text{-}9(17 - 7) \div \text{-}4 = $ _____

5) $21(4 \times \text{-}29) + \text{-}96(\text{-}82 - \text{-}4) = $ _____

(iv) Calculator Memory

The calculator has a number of memory functions:

- A **History Memory** of previous calculations (both expressions and results).
- An **Answer Memory** that stores the last calculation result obtained.
- An **Independent Memory** that allows you to store a value in the calculator which can be added to or subtracted from the result of an expression.

1. History Memory

The calculator can back-step to a previous calculation.

Example:
> Back-step through two calculations
> **265 − 167** and **666 + 88** to work back to
> **383 − 179**, the first calculation keyed in.

The calculator displays the last calculation keyed in.

```
265 − 167


              98
```

Step 1: Press ▲ to back-step to the previous sum.

```
666 + 88


             754
```

Step 2: Press ▲ to back-step to the previous sum.

```
383 − 179


             204
```

The calculator now displays the original calculation:

383 − 179 = 204

Important Note

The calculator memory contents are cleared whenever the calculator is **turned off** or **turned on** or the calculator is **reset**.

The calculator memory is also limited. If the calculation memory history becomes full, the oldest calculation is deleted automatically to make room for a new calculation.

2. Answer Memory

The **Answer Memory** can be used to perform a series of calculations and yield an overall answer at the end.

Example 1: | Divide the result of **8 × 16** by **4**.

Step 1: Press   **8**   **×**   **1**   **6**   **=**

> **8 × 16**
>
>   **128**

Step 2: Press   **÷**   to show **Ans** will be divided by.

> **Ans ÷**

Step 3: Press   **4**   **=**   for the answer of **32**.

> **Ans ÷ 4**
>
>   **32**

The answer memory contents from one calculation can be inputted into an expression to solve another calculation.

Example 2: | Calculate **65 + 88** and then subtract the answer from **789**.

Step 1: Press   **6**   **5**   **+**   **8**   **8**   **=**

> **65 + 88**
>
>   **153**

Step 2: Press **7** **8** **9** **−** **Ans** **=**

789 − Ans
636

The calculator has performed two calculations:

Calculation 1 $65 + 88 = 153$

Calculation 2 $789 − 153 = 636$

Exercise 20: 7b   Answer using a calculator:

6) Multiply the result of **893 − 678** by **23**. _____

7) Add **299** to the result of **923 − 269**. _____

8) Calculate **13 × 153** then divide the answer by **9**. _____

9) Calculate **840 ÷ 14** then subtract the answer from **283**.
_____

10) Add **1067** and **497** then subtract the answer
from **3962**. _____

Score

3. Independent Memory

The **Independent Memory** in the calculator means you can add or subtract the displayed value or result of an expression to or from the independent memory. The memory contents can then be recalled to give an overall answer.

Example 1:

Add **23 + 9** to **53 − 6**, then subtract **45 × 2**, then add **99 ÷ 3** by making use of the independent memory.

$$23 + 9 = 32 \quad \text{(Add to memory)}$$
$$53 - 6 = 47 \quad \text{(Add to memory)}$$
$$45 \times 2 = 90 \quad \text{(Subract from memory)}$$
$$\underline{99 \div 3 = 33} \quad \text{(Add to memory)}$$
$$\textbf{Total} \quad \textbf{22} \quad \text{(Recalled from memory)}$$

The independent memory is operated by using the

  and buttons.

Step 1: Press

When **M+** is pressed **23 + 9 = 32** is added to memory.

> **23 + 9 M+**
>
> **32**

Step 2: Press

Now **53 – 6 = 47** has been added to memory.

> **53 – 6 M+**
>
> **47**

Step 3: Press

When **SHIFT M+(M–)** is pressed **45 × 2 = 90** has been subtracted from memory.

> **45 × 2 M–**
>
> **90**

Step 4: Press

Now **99 ÷ 3 = 33** has been added to memory.

> **99 ÷ 3 M+**
>
> **33**

Step 5: Press   to recall the memory which will have calculated the answer as **22**.

> **M**
>
> **22**

The independent memory is stored in the calculator until it is cleared. The symbol **M** appears on the display when there is a value other than zero stored in the calculator. The memory content is a variable that can be inserted into any calculation when required using a simple procedure.

Example 2: Store a value of **193** in the independent memory. Multiply this stored value by **69**, add **56** and then subtract the independent memory (**193**) from it.

Step 1: Press

> **69 × M + 56 − M**

Step 2: Press for the answer of **13,180**.

```
69 × M + 56 − M

                            13,180
```

The independent memory remains when the **AC** button is pressed and if the calculator is turned off. The calculator can be **cleared** by following this simple procedure.

Example 3: | Demonstrate the steps to clear the calculator's independent memory.

To clear the calculator press these four buttons in order.

1.	2.	3.	4.
	SHIFT	STO	M− M
0	◯	RCL	M+

The display shows **0→M** to indicate the memory is **0**.

```
0→M

                               0
```

Exercise 20: 8

Solve by using the independent memory of the calculator:

1) Add **33 × 12** to **208 ÷ 13**, then subtract **44 × 6** and then subtract **201 − 59**. _____

2) Add **447 − 219** to **1,207 ÷ 17**, then subtract **21 × 6** and then add **399 − 113**. _____

3) Subtract **557 + 654** from **396 ÷ 22** added to **98 × 12**, added to **752 − 487**. _____ (Do the additions first.)

4) Do the following calculation as directed below:

$$89 + 48 \quad \text{(Add to memory)}$$
$$53 \times 66 \quad \text{(Add to memory)}$$
$$34 \times 21 \quad \text{(Subtract from memory)}$$
$$\underline{630 \div 6} \quad \text{(Add to memory)}$$
Total \qquad (Recall from memory)

---

5) Add **211 × 11**, then subtract **208 + 667**, then subtract **42 × 9** and then add **6120 ÷ 90**. _____

6) Do the following calculation as directed below:

$$75 \times 108 \quad \text{(Add to memory)}$$
$$64 + 972 \quad \text{(Subtract from memory)}$$
$$654 \div 3 \quad \text{(Add to memory)}$$
$$\underline{32 \times 84} \quad \text{(Subtract from memory)}$$
Total \qquad (Recall from memory)

Do the following calculations by storing an independent memory value first:

7) Store **269** in the independent memory.
   Multiply the stored value by **208**, then subtract **388** and then add on the stored value. _____

8) Store **825** in the independent memory.
   Multiply the stored value by **72**, then add **4009** and then subtract the stored value. _____

9) Store **620** in the independent memory.
   Divide the stored value by **4**, multiply by **12**, then subtract **219** and then add the stored value. _____

10) Store **427** in the independent memory.
    Multiply **208** and **51**, then divide by **6** and then add on the stored value. _____

Score

c. Decimals
(i) Four Rules of Decimals

The calculator automatically judges the calculation priority by applying the BIDMAS or BODMAS rules for + − × ÷ decimal calculations. The calculator displays the answer as a fraction but this can easily be converted to a decimal.

Example: | Calculate $82 \div 8 \times 3.6$. Give your answer as a decimal and not an improper fraction.

Press to toggle between the answer as an improper fraction and a decimal.

$82 \div 8 \times 3.6$		$82 \div 8 \times 3.6$
$\dfrac{369}{10}$		36.9

Exercise 20: 9 Answer using a calculator:

Score

1) $558 \div 6 - 28 \times 3 = $ _____

2) $72 \div 4 \div 12 \times 8 = $ _____

3) $85 \times 8 \div 4 \times 7 = $ _____

4) $20 + 6 \times 9 \div 5 = $ _____

5) $8.6 - 6 \times 2 + 9.7 = $ _____

6) $4.2 \times 8.4 - 4 \div 2.5 = $ _____

7) $3 \times 6.81 \div 4 \times 8 = $ _____

8) $39 \times 3.9 \div 1.8 \times 5 = $ _____

9) $22 \div 7.5 \times 99.9 = $ _____

10) $87.2 + 4.5 \times 5.58 = $ _____

(ii) Specifying the Number of Decimal Places

The calculator can be fixed to display an answer to any number of decimal places from 0 to 9. If a fix is programmed into the calculator, each calculation result is rounded to the specified digit before being displayed.

In **COMP** (default) mode, decimal places are not fixed.

This calculation is not fixed: $100 \div 7 = $ **14.285714**

Fixed at 3 decimal places   = **14.286** (to 3 d.p.)

Fixed at 2 decimal places   = **14.29** (to 2 d.p.)

Fixed at 1 decimal place   = **14.3**   (to 1 d.p.)

Example: | Fix the calculator to display all answers to 2 decimal places.

SHIFT   MODE   SET UP

Step 1:   Press   ◯   ◯   to display the first screen.

1: Mth10	**2: Line10**
3: Deg	**4: Rad**
5: Gra	**6: Fix**
7: Sci	**8: Norm**

Step 2:   Press **6** **Fix**   the number of decimal places.

Fix   0 ~ 9?

Step 3:   Press **2** to display results to 2 decimal places.

Press $a\frac{b}{c} \Leftrightarrow \frac{d}{c}v$ to toggle between the answer as an improper
       S⇔D   fraction, a decimal with no fixed places and a
       decimal with the fixed places.

Exercise 20: 10   Answer the following questions.

Fix the calculator at 1 decimal place:

Score

1) **54.8 $\div$ 5 $\times$ 3.6 =** _____   2) **83 $\div$ 4.5 $\div$ 1.2 =** _____

3) $21 \times 7.2 \div 4.8 =$ _____   4) $9.99 + 68.2 \times 9.6 =$ _____

Fix the calculator at 2 decimal places:
5) $88.7 - 11.89 \times 4.8 =$ _____   6) $5.98 \div 4 \times 80.7 =$ _____

7) $41 \div 2.3 \times 28.4 =$ _____   8) $9.2 + 6.71 \times 7.3 =$ _____

Fix the calculator at 3 decimal places:
9) $88.7 - 1.8 \div 3.9 =$ _____   10) $12 \div 3.4 \times 7.68 =$ _____

d. Fractions
(i) Specifying the Input/Output Format

Fractions can be expressed in **Maths Format** or **Line Format**.
Maths format will show a fraction in a 'natural' way.

In maths format **'one and two thirds'** would be displayed as: $1\frac{2}{3}$

Line format will show a fraction in a linear way with markers.

In line format **'one and two thirds'** would be displayed as: $1 \lrcorner 2 \lrcorner 3$

In **COMP** (default) mode, the calculator will automatically display fractions in maths format. However, the Input/Output Format can be changed by following a simple process.

Example: Demonstrate how to set the input/output format.

                    SHIFT   MODE   SET UP
Step 1:   Press 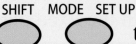 to display the first screen.

1: Mth10	**2: Line10**
3: Deg	**4: Rad**
5: Gra	**6: Fix**
7: Sci	**8: Norm**

Step 2: Choose the format you require.

For maths format: **1: Mth IO** Press

For linear format: **2: Line IO** Press

(ii) Entering Fractions into the Calculator
1. Using the Maths Format

Example 1: | Input the fraction $\frac{3}{4}$ into the calculator.

Step 1: Press 3 ▽ 4

$\frac{3}{4}$

Step 2: Press ▬ $\frac{3}{4}$

$\frac{3}{4}$

$\frac{3}{4}$

Example 2: | Input the mixed number $1\frac{4}{5}$ into the calculator.

Step 1: Press 1 ▷ 4 ▽ 5

$1\frac{4}{5}$

Step 2: Press ▬ $\frac{9}{5}$

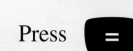

$$1\frac{4}{5}$$

$$\frac{9}{5}$$

Note: Mixed numbers are displayed as improper fractions.

Exercise 20: 11a Practise entering the following fractions into the calculator using the maths format:

1) $\frac{3}{4}$ 2) $\frac{4}{7}$ 3) $6\frac{1}{2}$ 4) $5\frac{5}{9}$ 5) $14\frac{7}{12}$

_____   _____   _____   _____   _____

2. Using the Linear Format

Example 1: Input the fraction $\frac{3}{4}$ into the calculator.

Step 1:   Press   **3**  **4**

> 3 ⌐4
>
>   0

Step 2:   Press   **=** **3 ⌐4**

> 3 ⌐4
>
>   3 ⌐4

Example 2: Input the mixed number $1\frac{4}{5}$ into the calculator.

Step 1:   Press   **1** **4** **5**

```
1 ⌐ 4 ⌐ 5



                                          0
```

Step 2: Press ⬛= **9 ⌐ 5**

```
1 ⌐ 4 ⌐ 5



                                   9 ⌐ 5
```

Note: Mixed numbers are displayed as improper fractions.

Exercise 20: 11b Enter the following fractions into the calculator using the line format:

6) $\frac{2}{3}$ 7) $\frac{5}{8}$ 8) $4\frac{2}{7}$ 9) $3\frac{7}{10}$ 10) $11\frac{3}{5}$

_____ _____ _____ _____ _____

(iii) Toggling Between Fraction Display Formats

In **COMP** (default) mode all fractions are automatically displayed as improper fractions when the equals sign is pressed. It is possible to change the fraction to either a mixed number or a decimal by following a simple procedure.

Example: Input $2\frac{3}{5}$ as an improper fraction, then use the toggle button to change it into a mixed number, then into a decimal.

Inputting $2\frac{3}{5}$ as an improper fraction.

Step 1: Press

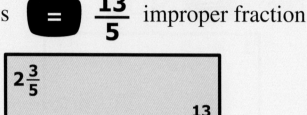

$2\frac{3}{5}$

Step 2: Press **=** $\frac{13}{5}$ improper fraction

$2\frac{3}{5}$

$\frac{13}{5}$

Changing $\frac{13}{5}$ to a mixed number using the toggle button.

Step 3: Press SHIFT Use the toggle button for a mixed number $a\frac{b}{c} \Leftrightarrow \frac{d}{c}y$ S⇔D $2\frac{3}{5}$ Mixed Number

$2\frac{3}{5}$

$2\frac{3}{5}$

Changing $2\frac{3}{5}$ to a decimal using the toggle button.

Step 4: Press Use the toggle button for a decimal. $a\frac{b}{c} \Leftrightarrow \frac{d}{c}y$ S⇔D **2.6** Decimal

$2\frac{3}{5}$

2.6

(iv) Setting the Fraction Display Format

The **Fraction Display Format** can be set so it displays all fractions that are bigger than a whole one as either mixed numbers or improper fractions. If the toggle button is pressed it will always show the equivalent decimal value.

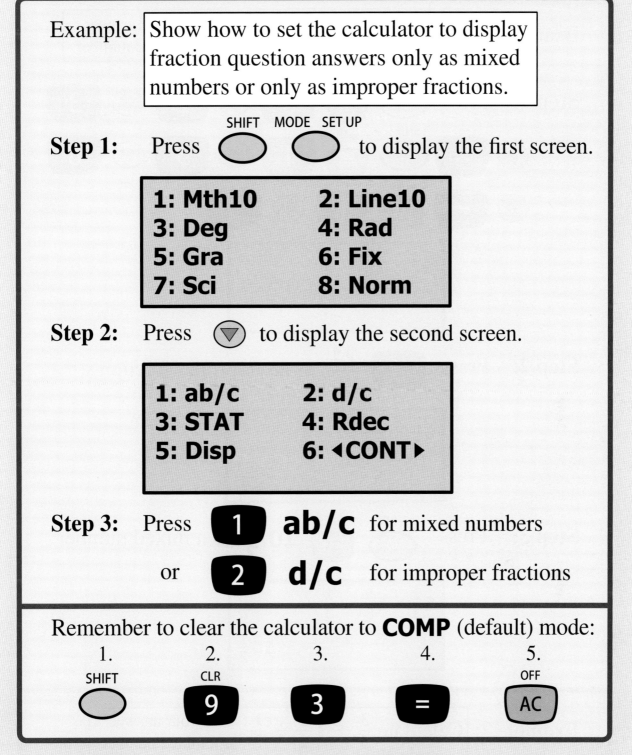

Example: Show how to set the calculator to display fraction question answers only as mixed numbers or only as improper fractions.

Step 1: Press ⬭ SHIFT ⬭ MODE SET UP to display the first screen.

1: Mth10	2: Line10
3: Deg	4: Rad
5: Gra	6: Fix
7: Sci	8: Norm

Step 2: Press ▽ to display the second screen.

1: ab/c	2: d/c
3: STAT	4: Rdec
5: Disp	6: ◄CONT►

Step 3: Press **1** **ab/c** for mixed numbers

or **2** **d/c** for improper fractions

Remember to clear the calculator to **COMP** (default) mode:

1.	2.	3.	4.	5.
SHIFT	CLR			OFF
⬭	**9**	**3**	**=**	AC

(v) The Four Rules of Fractions

The calculator can add, subtract, multiply and divide fractions in either maths format or linear format. Maths format displays the fractions as they are written and this workbook will focus on working in this way. The calculator automatically applies the BODMAS/BIDMAS rules.

Example 1: Calculate $6\frac{2}{3} \times 1\frac{5}{8} - \frac{1}{3}$ Give your answer as a mixed number.

Step 1: Press

$$6\frac{2}{3} \times 1\frac{5}{8} - \frac{1}{3}$$

Step 2: Press [=] $\frac{21}{2}$ as an improper fraction

$$6\frac{2}{3} \times 1\frac{5}{8} - \frac{1}{3}$$
$$\frac{21}{2}$$

Step 3: Press SHIFT [S⇔D] $10\frac{1}{2}$ as a mixed number

$$6\frac{2}{3} \times 1\frac{5}{8} - \frac{1}{3}$$
$$10\frac{1}{2}$$

Example 2: Calculate $\frac{3}{5} + 1\frac{1}{2} \div \frac{1}{3}$ Give your answer as a mixed number.

Step 1: Press ▣ [3] ▽ [5]

▷ [÷] ▣ [1] ▽ [3]

$$\frac{3}{5} + 1\frac{1}{2} \div \frac{1}{3}$$

Step 2: Press **=** $\frac{51}{10}$ as an improper fraction

$$\frac{3}{5} + 1\frac{1}{2} \div \frac{1}{3}$$

$$\frac{51}{10}$$

Step 3: Press SHIFT $5\frac{1}{10}$ as a mixed number

$$\frac{3}{5} + 1\frac{1}{2} \div \frac{1}{3}$$

$$5\frac{1}{10}$$

Exercise 20 : 12 Calculate the following:

Score

Give your answers as mixed numbers.

1) $1\frac{1}{3} - \frac{3}{10} \times 2\frac{1}{2} =$ ___

2) $2\frac{2}{3} + 3\frac{1}{6} \div 5\frac{1}{4} =$ ___

3) $1\frac{1}{2} + 2\frac{1}{10} \div 3\frac{3}{5} =$ ___

4) $2\frac{5}{8} \times \frac{5}{7} \div 1\frac{1}{2} =$ ___

5) $\frac{5}{8} \times 3\frac{1}{3} - 1\frac{3}{5} =$ ___

6) $2\frac{1}{6} + 1\frac{3}{4} - 3\frac{2}{3} =$ ___

7) $1\frac{5}{9} \div 1\frac{1}{6} + 1\frac{3}{4} =$ ___

8) $1\frac{1}{20} \div 1\frac{1}{2} + 1\frac{1}{5} =$ ___

9) $4\frac{1}{2} + 5\frac{3}{10} \times 2\frac{3}{7} =$ ___

10) $4\frac{1}{5} \times 4\frac{5}{6} \times 4\frac{1}{6} =$ ___

e. Percentages

Percentage Calculations can be performed on the calculator. Percentages are fully explained earlier (see Maths Workbook 3). All percentage calculations are of only two main types:

either

Percentage to Amount - find a percentage of a given amount

or

Amount to Percentage - find a given amount as a percentage

(i) Percentage to Amount

Percentage to Amount questions mean a percentage of a given amount has to be found.

Example: | What is **36%** of **250**?

The question could be written out in the following way if we were following the standard procedure from Maths Workbook 3:

$$\% \longrightarrow Am$$

$$\frac{36}{100} \times \frac{250}{1}$$

When working out the percentage using the calculator it is important to follow the same steps as the written method.

In other words, as it is said: **36% of (×) 250**

Step 1: Press

SHIFT   %

[3] [6] (SHIFT) [( ]

[×] [2] [5] [0]

| 36% × 250 |

© 2011 Stephen Curran ae

Step 2: Press **90** is the amount (**36%** of **250**)

36% × 250

90

Exercise 20: 13a Find the amount:

1) **6%** of **£51**. £_____

2) **29%** of **67**. _____

3) **21%** of $7\frac{2}{3}$. _____

4) **11.5%** of **£6**. £_____

5) **104%** of **450kg**. _____kg

(ii) Amount to Percentage

Amount to Percentage questions mean a percentage has to be found from a given amount.

Example: What is **90** as a percentage of **250**?

The question could be written out in the following way if we were following the standard procedure from Maths Workbook 3:

$$Am \longrightarrow \%$$

$$\frac{90}{250} \times \frac{100}{1}$$

When working out the percentage using the calculator it is important to follow the same steps as the written method.

In other words, as it is said: **90 ÷ 250 of (×) 100%**

Step 1: Press

SHIFT   %

There is no need to multiply
as this is incorporated in shift.

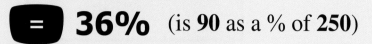

$$90 \div 250\%$$

Step 2: Press **=** **36%** (is **90** as a % of **250**)

$$90 \div 250\%$$

$$36\%$$

Exercise 20: 13b Find the following percentages:

6) **17** as a % of **20**. ____%   7) **162** as a % of **720**. ____%

8) **3.5** as a % of **70**. ____%   9) **35** as a % of **56**. ____%

10) **156** as a % of **240**. ____%   Score

---

f. Powers and Roots
(i) Squares, Cubes and Indices

Here is a quick reminder of what was taught in Maths Workbook 1.

A **Square Number** is a number multiplied by itself once.

$$12 \times 12 = 12^2 = 144$$

A **Cube Number** is a number multiplied by itself twice.

$$4 \times 4 \times 4 = 4^3 = 64$$

Indices are the collective name given to any power or index. If we take **3** to the power of **4**, the **4** would be index or power which determines how many times it is multiplied by itself.

$$3 \times 3 \times 3 \times 3 = 3^4 = 81$$

Inputting square, cube and other indices or powers can be done very simply in the following way:

Example 1: What is the square of **22** (or 22^2)?

Step 1: Press

22^2

Step 2: Press ▭= for the answer of **484**.

22^2

484

Example 2: What is the cube of **13** (or 13^3)?

Step 1: Press

Step 2: Press ▭= for the answer of **2,197**.

Example 3: What is **5** to the power of **4** (or 5^4)?

Step 1: Press   ▭4

Step 2: Press ▭= for the answer of **625**.

Exercise 20: 14a Answer the following:

1) $14^2 + 3^4 =$ _____

2) $16^3 - 798 + 5^5 =$ _____

3) $3.5^2 \times 7 + 12^2 =$ _____

4) $14^3 \div 20 - 4^3 =$ _____

5) $3(7^2 + 2^3) \div 5 =$ _____

(ii) Square, Cube and Higher Power Roots

Here is another reminder of what was taught in Maths Workbook 1. **Square, Cube and Higher Power Roots/Indices** are inverse operations of finding a square, cube or higher power.

A **Square Root** is the origin of a square number.

$$12 \times 12 = 12^2 = 144 \longrightarrow \sqrt{144} = 12$$

144 originated from **12** and so **12** is the square root of **144**.

A **Cube Root** is the origin of a cube number.

$$4 \times 4 \times 4 = 4^3 = 64 \longrightarrow \sqrt[3]{64} = 4$$

64 originated from **4** and so **4** is the cube root of **144**.

Roots of Indices or **Higher Powers** are the origins of indices or higher power numbers.

$$3 \times 3 \times 3 \times 3 = 3^4 = 81 \longrightarrow \sqrt[4]{81} = 3$$

81 originated from **3** and so **3** is the index root of **81**.

Inputting square, cube and higher power roots/indices is a simple process and can be done in the following way:

Example 1: | What is the square root of **784** (or $\sqrt{784}$)?

Step 1: Press

$$\sqrt{784}$$

Step 2: Press for the answer of **28**.

$$\sqrt{784}$$

28

Example 2: What is the cube root of **6,859** (or $\sqrt[3]{6859}$)?

Step 1: Press (SHIFT) $\boxed{\sqrt[3]{\blacksquare}}$ $\boxed{6}$ $\boxed{8}$ $\boxed{5}$ $\boxed{9}$

Step 2: Press $\boxed{=}$ for the answer of **19**.

Example 3: What is the sixth index root of **729** (or $\sqrt[6]{729}$)?

Step 1: Press (SHIFT) $\boxed{\sqrt[\blacksquare]{\blacksquare}}$ $\boxed{6}$ $\boxed{\triangleright}$ $\boxed{7}$ $\boxed{2}$ $\boxed{9}$

Step 2: Press $\boxed{=}$ for the answer of **3**.

Exercise 20: 14b Answer the following:

6) $\sqrt{2500} + 3^7 = \underline{\hspace{2cm}}$

7) $3^6 \times \sqrt[5]{16807} = \underline{\hspace{2cm}}$

8) $17^2 - 214 + \sqrt[3]{729} = \underline{\hspace{2cm}}$

9) $\sqrt{4.84} \div 5 + 8.9 = \underline{\hspace{2cm}}$

10) $2(8^3 + 4^4) \times \sqrt[4]{4096} = \underline{\hspace{2cm}}$

Score $\boxed{}$

g. Circle Formulae

Here is a quick reminder of the **Circle Formulae** from Maths Workbook 5. It is possible to find the area, circumference and radius of a circle using the value of π (**pi**) = **3.142**

To find the area of a circle use this formula:
$$\textbf{Area} = \pi \times \textbf{r}^2$$

To find the circumference of a circle use this formula:
$$\textbf{Circumference} = \pi \times \textbf{D}$$

To find the diameter of a circle use this formula:
$$\textbf{Diameter} = \textbf{C} \div \pi$$

The calculator is able to calculate the area, circumference and diameter of circles.

Example 1:

Find the area of a circle that has a radius of **3cm** to 2 d.p.

3cm

This circle is not drawn to scale.

Step 1: Press ⬭(SHIFT) [x10^x](π e) [×] [3] [x^2]

$$\pi \times 3^2$$

28.274

Step 2: Press [=] [S⇔D]($a\frac{b}{c}$⇔$\frac{d}{c}$y) for the answer of **28.27cm²**.

$$\pi \times 3^2$$

28.27433388

Example 2: Find the circumference of a circle that has a diameter of **6cm** to 2 d.p.

Step 1: Press ⬭(SHIFT) [x10^x](π e) [×] [6]

Step 2: Press [=] [S⇔D]($a\frac{b}{c}$⇔$\frac{d}{c}$y) for the answer of **18.85cm**.

Example 3: Find the diameter of a circle that has a circumference of **18.85cm**.

Step 1: Press [1] [8] [•] [8] [5]

[÷] ⬭(SHIFT) [x10^x](π e)

Step 2: Press [=] [S⇔D]($a\frac{b}{c}$⇔$\frac{d}{c}$y) for the answer of **6cm**.

Exercise 20: 15 Answer the following:

1) What is the circumference of this circle to 2 d.p.? _____ cm (Convert to cm.)

85mm

This circle is not drawn to scale.

2) Calculate the area of a circle with a diameter of **3.2m**. _____ m² (Round to a whole number.)

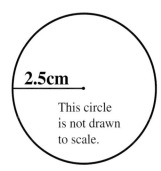

2.5cm

This circle is not drawn to scale.

Calculate the area and circumference of this circle to 3 d.p.:

3) The area   = _____ cm²

4) The circumference = _____ cm

5) If the circumference of a circle is **47.12m**, then what will the radius be to 1 d.p.? _____ m

What is the area and the perimeter of this semi-circle to 1 d.p.?

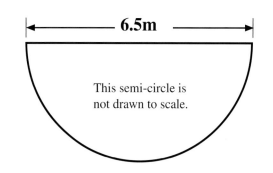

6.5m

This semi-circle is not drawn to scale.

6) The area   = _____ m²

7) The perimeter = _____ m

If the diameter of this cylinder is **75mm** and its length is **140mm**, find the following to 2 d.p.:

Remember: a formula for all prisms
Volume = Area of one Side × Length

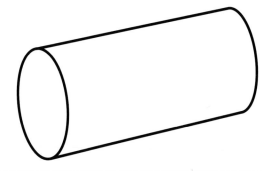

8) The total area of both ends = _____ cm²

9) The circumference of one circular end = _____ cm

10) The volume of the cylinder = _____ cm³

Chapter Twenty-one
REVISION

1. Basic Number

Exercise 21: 1   Answer the following:

1) a) Write in figures the number **thirteen thousand and ninety three**. _____

   b) Write in words the number **423,296**. _____

   _____

   _____

2) a)   **40062**
          7985 −
          _____
          _____

   b)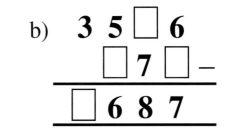

3) a) What is the greatest number that can be made by arranging the digits **8, 1, 9, 3**? _____

   b) By how much smaller is this number than **15,000**?

   _____

4) a)   **7956**
            7 ×
          _____

          _____

   b)   **358**
          69 ×
          - - - - - - - -

          _____

          _____

5) a) Multiply **289** by **100**. _____

   b) **43,900 ÷ 100** = _____

6) a) **356 × 72** = _____

   b) Which of the following numbers is the answer closest to? Underline the correct answer.

   2,450   28,000   210,000   2,800   21,000

7) a) $8\overline{)416}$ b) **598 ÷ 22** = _____ rem ____

8) a) **306 ÷ 17** = _____

   b) **17 × 18** = _____

   c) **300 ÷ 100** = _____

9) a) I think of a number then double it. Next I subtract **6**. The answer is **14**. What was the number I started with? _____

   b) If we treble a number and subtract **10** the answer is **47**. What is the number? _____

10) a) Divide the product of **968** and **3** by **4**, then subtract **93**. _____

    b) Multiply the quotient of **273** and **13** by **10**, then add **16**. _____

Score

2. Number Relationships

Exercise 21: 2 Answer the following:

1)

A		34
		24
B	18	

96 ← B 18

↓
96

When every square in the grid is filled, each row and column adds up to **96**.

a) What is the value of **A**? _____

b) What is the value of **B**? _____

---

2) a) What is **19²**? _____

b) What is the square root of **169**? ($\sqrt{169}$) _____

---

3) a) What is **4⁶**? Underline the correct answer.

24   **16,324**   **4,096**   **1,024**   **256**

b) A number is multiplied by itself. The answer is then multiplied by the original number. The new number is **125**. What is the original number? _____

---

4) a) Add the prime numbers between **12** and **20**. _____

b) List the rectangular numbers between **5** and **19**.

_____

---

5) a) How many dots will there be in pattern 12? _____

b) Write the next two numbers in the sequence.

42   **26**   **16**   **10**   **6**   _4_   _2_

6) a) How many hexagons will the next shape in the sequence have?

17   26   31   37   45

b) How many matchsticks are needed to make the next shape in the sequence? _____

7) a) Which pair of numbers has the greatest difference?

(**14** and **3**)   (**6** and **-8**)   (**40** and **30**)

(**-4** and **-11**)   (**9** and **-4**)   _____

b) Using the number line calculate **-5 +9 -4**. _____

-5   -4   -3   -2   -1   0   1   2   3   4   5

8) a) Write the group of numbers below that are all multiples of either **3** or **5**.

(**8, 10, 12**)   (**15, 18, 20**)   (**12, 14, 15**)
(**20, 24, 26**)   (**18, 20, 22**)   _____

b) Name all the factors of **48**. _____

9) a) What is the highest common factor (HCF) of **78** and **143**?

_____

b) What is the lowest common multiple (LCM) of **9** and **14**?

_____

10) a) A book has **324** pages. If you read **12** pages a day, how long will it take to finish the book? _____ days

b) In a school **20** children eat **4** bags of boiled sweets in a week. At this same rate, how many bags of boiled sweets would **60** children eat in **5** weeks? _____ bags

3. Decimals

Exercise 21: 3 Answer the following:

1) a) What is the value of the **9** in the number **4.879**?

   _____ (in written form)

   b) Express the number **5.29** in units and hundredths.

   _____

2) a) Underline the number that has the least value.

   -22.8   **-57.4**   **-23**   **320**   **-1.99**

   b) Place **1.09**, **1.9** and **1.009** in order, smallest first.

   _____   _____   _____

3) a) Round **4.869** to 2 decimal places. _____

   b) Round **0.93** to 1 decimal place. _____

4) a) Which arrow is pointing at **5.04** on this number line?

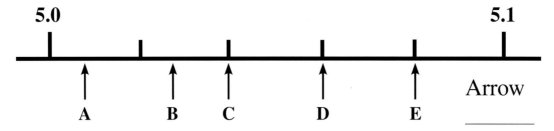

   5.0 .... **5.1**

   A   B   C   D   E   Arrow _____

   b) Which sign should be placed between these numbers?

   < or **>**   **-2.6**   **-3.2**

5) a) Add **9.432** to **84.9**. _____

   b) What is the difference between **3.864** and **23.79**?

   _____

6) a) Underline the product of **0.99** and **14.2**.
(Answer correct to 2 d.p.)

13.06   **14.06**   **14.058**   **1,024**   **14.05**

b) Give an estimate of this sum in the right order of magnitude:

$$502.1 \div 4.9 \approx \underline{\hspace{3cm}}$$

7) a) What is **12.72** divided by **30** to 1 decimal place?

_____

b) What is **3.468** + **1.458** to 2 decimal places? _____

8) a) Which operation has changed **346** to **3.46**?

$\times$**100** $\times$**0.01** $\times$**0.001** $\times$**10** $\times$**0.1**

b) Underline the correct answer to **13.6 $\div$ 1000**.

136   **1.36**   **0.00136**   **0.0136**   **0.136**

9) a) Which one of these numbers is equal to $\mathbf{0.57 \times 10^2}$?

5.7   **570**   **5.7 $\times$ 100**   **0.57 $\times$ 100**   **5.7 $\div$ 10**

b) Find the quotient of **28.6** by **5.2**. _____

10) a) Which of the following is equal to: (Answer to 2 d.p.)

$$\mathbf{(0.57 \times 2.4) - 1.3}$$

0.17   **0.07**   **0.068**   **0.08**   **0.1**

b) Underline the number that is closest to **7**.

7.1   **7.001**   **6.998**   **7.09**   **6.901**

Score

4. Fractions

Exercise 21: 4   Answer the following:

1) a) Simplify $\dfrac{36}{57}$ ____   b) $\dfrac{7}{8} = \dfrac{42}{?}$ ____

---

2) a) Change to an improper fraction:

$5\dfrac{6}{7}$ ____

b) Change to a mixed number:

$\dfrac{68}{10}$ ____

---

3) a) $3\dfrac{3}{5} + 2\dfrac{7}{9}$ b) $6\dfrac{1}{3} - 4\dfrac{8}{9}$

= ____   = ____

---

4) a) $6\dfrac{1}{2} \times 2\dfrac{2}{3}$ b) $3\dfrac{2}{3} \div 1\dfrac{1}{4}$

= ____   = ____

---

5) a) Find the fractional part: $\dfrac{4}{5}$ of **250** ____

b) Find the whole when: $\dfrac{6}{7}$ is **210** ____

---

6) a) Change to fractions:

3.24 ____

b) Change to decimals:

$\dfrac{6}{7}$ ____

(to 2 d.p.)

7) a) Place these fractions in size order, smallest first.

$\frac{7}{8}$ $\frac{6}{7}$ $\frac{8}{9}$ $\frac{5}{6}$ ____ ____ ____ ____

b) Order these decimals and fractions, largest first.

$\frac{3}{7}$ **0.45** $\frac{2}{5}$ **0.39** ____ ____ ____ ____

8) a) Multiply $3\frac{3}{7}$ by the difference between $3\frac{2}{3}$ and $1\frac{4}{5}$. ____

b) Find the quotient of $4\frac{1}{8}$ and $1\frac{5}{6}$ then subtract $\frac{3}{10}$. —

9) a) When $\frac{5}{8}$ of a certain number is increased by **37** the result is **82**. What is the number?

The number is _____ .

Given Fraction	Missing Fraction
Amount	Amount
Total	One Part

b) Magda shared out some stickers with her friend Anushka. She kept **33** stickers for herself and gave $\frac{4}{7}$ to Anushka. How many stickers did she start with? _____ stickers

10) Calculate the following fractions and decimals.

Write as fractions.

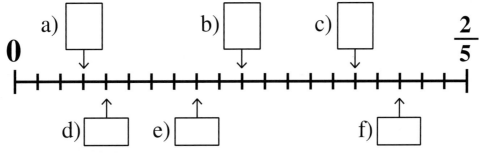

Write as decimals.

5. Money and Costs

Exercise 21: 5 Answer the following:

1) a) **£4.59** is _____ p.   b) **87p** is £ _____ .

2) a) **£9.26 + 243p** = £ _____   b) **£8.17 − 49p** = _____ p

3) a) **£2.24 × 37** = £ _____   b) **£49.76 ÷ 8** = £ _____

4) a) **392p − £1.46** = £ _____   b) **3.2 × £4.20** = _____ p

5) a) Ian spends **£3.67** on sweets and **£2.25** on cola in a shop. How much change from **£10** does he receive? £ _____

   b) **7** children went on a school boat trip. The total ticket cost was **£89.25**. What did each child pay? £ _____

6) a) If it costs **£2.89** to send a certain type of parcel, how much will it cost to send **8** similar parcels? £ _____

   b) A day at an amusement park costs **£17** for adults and children are half price. How much will it cost Mr and Mrs Lee and their **3** children to go to the park? £ _____

7) **21** crates of lemonade cost **£1,365**. How much would:
   a) **12** crates cost? £ _____   b) **30** crates cost? £ _____

8) Manraj changes some pounds to US dollars. He receives **$60** for **£39**. a) The exchange rate is _____ p to the $.
                    b) He would receive $ _____ for **£91**.

9) A toy store buys **50** dolls from a wholesaler at **£7.50** each.
   a) What is the profit if all are sold at **£13.99** each? £ _____
   b) What is the loss if only **10** dolls are sold? £ _____

10) A supermarket sells baked beans in **415g** tins for **68p**.
    a) The unit cost per kg to the nearest penny is £ _____ .
    b) Four tins wrapped together are sold for **£2.49**. What is the new unit cost? £ _____

6. Measurement

Exercise 21: 6 Answer the following: Score [   ]

1) a) **2.5kg** = _____ g   b) **150mℓ** = _____ cℓ

2) a) **4030m** = ____ km ____ cm b) **3.5cℓ** = _____ mℓ

3) a) **36g** = _____ kg   b) **7463cℓ** = ____ ℓ ____ mℓ

4) a) **4.79m** = _____ cm   b) **3427g** = _____ kg

5) a) **5.26km** = ____ km ____ m b) **4.51kg** = _____ g

6) a) **9.6cℓ** = _____ ℓ b) **426mm** = _____ m

7) a) **13** boys came to Jack's birthday party. Including Jack, they each drank a **333mℓ** can of juice. **Half** of them then drank one **200mℓ** cup of tea each. How many litres did they drink altogether? _____ ℓ

   b) Fern walked **2,750m** to and from school each day. How many kilometres did Fern walk in one normal school week? _____ km

8) a) Paul's vegetable patch is **3** metres in length. What would be the approximate length in feet? _____ ft

   b) Year 6 went on a **12.5** mile sponsored walk. Roughly how far is this in kilometres? _____ km

9) a) What is the likely weight of Trudy's school satchel?
      5kg   40g   2kg   500g   9kg   _____

   b) A child's paddling pool is likely to have a capacity of
      10,000ℓ 50ℓ 500mℓ 1,000ℓ 1,500cℓ   _____ .

10) What is the length of the black line in
   a) _____ cm? b) _____ m?

7. Averages

Exercise 21: 7 Answer the following:

1) Find the mode, median and mean of the following:

13   4   5   3   11   8   5   8   11   4   7   5   7

a) Mode: _____   b) Median: _____   c) Mean: _____

2) This is a record of temperatures during one week in August:

Monday	Tuesday	Wednesday	Thursday	Friday	Saturday	Sunday
26	28	24	27	20	29	28

a) What is the average temperature for the week? _____ °

b) Give the range of temperatures over the week. _____ °

3) Find the mean of the following numbers:

a) **6.5   8.25   1.8   9   1.25   9.2**   _____

b) **230   610   540   1,050   755**   _____

4) a) The average pocket money **9** boys received per week
   was **£10**. One boy received **£18** per week. What was
   the average pocket money for the other **8** boys? £ _____

   b) The mean intake of water of **6** children was **1,500mℓ** a
   day. **Two** of the children drank **1.75ℓ** each, **one** drank
   1,200mℓ and another **two** drank **1.3ℓ** each. How much
   did the sixth child drink? _____ litres

5) a) In a certain year in England the mean
   number of days it rained during one
   season was **45** days. How many days
   did it rain in the winter? _____ days

Season	Rainy Days
Spring	48 days
Summer	31 days
Autumn	39 days
Winter	? days

   b) What was the average number of days it rained per
   month during the year? _____ days

6) a) The mean height of **six** boys was **1.52m**. If all their heights were added together what would the total be? _____cm

b) The average cost of **5** tennis rackets was **£112**. What was the total cost of the tennis rackets? £_____

7) A supermarket sells **5** different varieties of super-sized chocolate bar. They are priced as follows:

£1.85   **£2.60**   **£1.70**   **£2.35**   **£3.80**

a) What is the median price of chocolate bars? £_____

b) Find the mean price of chocolate bars. £_____

8) Find the average of the following numbers:

a) **225, 199, 998, 751, 154, 836** and **421** _____

b) **8, 1, 5, 55, 2, 1, 34, 21, 3** and **13** _____

9) The sunshine hours were recorded over one week in July:

Monday	Tuesday	Wednesday	Thursday	Friday	Saturday	Sunday
10	4	10	14	12	?	9

The mean number of sunshine hours for the week is **10** hours.

a) There were _____ hours of sunshine on Saturday.

b) If the total number of sunshine hours over the four week period in July was **295** hours (including the hours stated on the table), what was the average sunshine hours for the other three weeks? _____

10) Five children's heights are as follows:

1.2m   118cm   133cm   1.41m   1.18m

a) What is the mode height? _____cm

b) The mean height is _____m.

8. Bases

Exercise 21: 8 Answer the following:

1) a) Convert 39_{10} to base 2.   b) Convert 11010_2 to base 10.

———$_2$ ———$_{10}$

2) a) $\begin{array}{r} 10011_2 \\ 10111_2 + \\ \hline \end{array}$

———$_2$

   b) $\begin{array}{r} 101010_2 \\ 1111_2 - \\ \hline \end{array}$

———$_2$

3) a) $\begin{array}{r} 10011_2 \\ 11_2 \times \\ \hline \end{array}$

   - - - - - - - - - - - - - - - - -

   ———

   ———$_2$

   b) $110_2 \overline{)111110_2}$ $^r.$ $_2$ $_2$

4) a) Convert 55_{10} to base 3.   b) Convert 2212_3 to base 10.

———$_3$ ———$_{10}$

5) a) $1201_3 + 221_3 =$ ———$_3$ b) $2021_3 - 222_3 =$ ———$_3$

6) a) $211_3 \times 12_3 =$ ———$_3$ b) $10021_3 \div 2_3 =$ ———$_3$

7) a) Convert 277_{10} to base 5.   b) Convert 113_5 to base 10.

———$_5$ ———$_{10}$

8) a) $240_5 + 314_5 =$ ———$_5$ b) $331_5 - 143_5 =$ ———$_5$

9) a) $321_5 \times 14_5 =$ ———$_5$ b) $2412_5 \div 3_5 =$ ———$_5$

10) Which base is used in these sums?

a) $\begin{array}{r} 1222 \\ 132 + \\ \hline 2020 \end{array}$ Base ———

b) $\begin{array}{r} 420 \\ 53 - \\ \hline 323 \end{array}$ Base ———

Score

9. Percentages

Exercise 21: 9 Answer the following:

1) a) Write **56%** as a fraction.   b) What is $\frac{5}{8}$ as a percentage?

_____   _____%

2) a) Find **22%** of **£5.50**.   b) Calculate **46%** of **310m**.

£ _____   _____km (to 3 d.p.)

3) a) Increase **£520** by **15%**.   b) Decrease **15kg** by **24%**.

£ _____   _____g

4) a) **260** is **65%** of which   b) If **35%** is **£2.10**, **100%**
   number? _____   would be £ _____ .

5) a) Express **156** as a %   b) What is **35m** as a %
   of **240**. _____%   of **5600cm**? _____%

6) a) If **500g** is increased to **2.25kg**, what is the percentage
   increase? _____%

   b) **£37.50** is decreased to **£30.75**. Calculate the percentage
   decrease. _____%

7) a) A family saved up **£3,200** for a holiday in America.
   They only spent **£1,440** on the holiday due to receiving
   a generous discount. What percentage of the original
   amount did they actually spend? _____%

   b) A local electronics shop is closing down and slashes
   all its prices by **35%**. How much would a television
   with an original price of **£750** cost? £ _____

8) a) **122%** as a decimal is

_1.22_ .

b) What is **0.09** as a %?

_9_ %

9) a) Place the following in size order, largest first.

$$\frac{6}{25} \qquad 26\% \qquad 0.23 \qquad \frac{7}{24} \overset{0.29}{} \qquad 0.3$$

____ ____ ____ ____ ____

b) Place the following in size order, smallest first.

$$6.1\% \qquad \frac{1}{20} \qquad 5.44\% \qquad \frac{2}{27} \qquad 0.04$$

____ ____ ____ ____ ____

10) a) Michael bought a computer game for **£125** with his birthday money. After some months he was bored with the game and sold it to his friend David for **£95**. What was Michael's percentage loss on the game? _24_ %

David kept the game for another six months and then he decided to sell it. He was able to sell it for **£152** due to a surge in the game's popularity. What was David's percentage gain on the game? _60_ %

b) A gardener had a **120ℓ** capacity water butt. Due to very little rainfall, he decided to top it up with tap water from the house. The water butt already had **15ℓ** in it. How full was it in percentage terms? _12.5_%

He travelled back and forth **five** times with containers and buckets and poured in the following amounts.

$$4.5\ell \qquad 6{,}700m\ell \qquad 9.25\ell \qquad 7.3\ell \qquad 5{,}250m\ell$$

How full, in percentage terms, was the water butt after he had done this? _88.0_%

 **Score**

10. Ratios

Exercise 21: 10 Answer the following:

1) a) Tina has **6** marbles. She gives **5** to her friend Sue. Write this as a ratio compared to the original amount.

_____ : _____

b) $\frac{2}{5}$ is a ratio that compares a quantity with the original whole amount. Write this quantity as a percentage.

_____%

Compare these quantities as ratios and fractions:

2) a) A train arrives at the station. **3** out of **13** of the carriages are 1st class and the rest are 2nd class.

_____ : _____

$\frac{3}{13}$ to _____

b) There are **9** colours on a paint pallette. Molly uses only **5** of them to paint with.

_____ : _____

to

_____ _____

---

3) a) Aman shares time on a computer game with his brother, Ibrahim, over a **6-hour** period. Aman uses it for $4\frac{1}{2}$ hours and Ibrahim for only $1\frac{1}{2}$ hours. Write their shares as a ratio and as a percentage.

_____ : _____   _____% : _____%

b) Write these percentage shares as ratios:

28% : 112% : 168%   _____ : _____ : _____

Find the ratios from these given amounts:

4) a) **£7.65 : 45p**

765	:	45
÷		÷
Ratio		
	:	

b) **0.2 : 2**

	:	
×		×
Ratio		
	:	

_____ : _____

_____ : _____

5) a) Tanveer and Rakesh share out **104** sweets in the ratio of **3 : 5**. How many sweets do they each receive?

Use this ratio box to help you.

Total	
Amount	:
Multiplier	
Ratio	:

_____ : _____

b) **4** out of every **9** boys in a class enjoy playing football. If **15** boys do not like playing football, how many boys are there altogether? _____ boys

6) a) **64** cakes are eaten at a children's birthday party. There are **12** boys and **14** girls in attendance. Each girl eats **2** cakes. How many does each boy eat? _____ cakes

Total	
Amount	: :
Multiplier	
Ratio	: :

b) Paul, Rumina and Lesley count the number of birds they each see in their garden in one day. Paul sees **5** times as many as Rumina who sees **3** times as many as Lesley. In all, they see **266** birds. How many birds do they each see?
Paul: _____ Rumina: _____ Lesley: _____

7) a) If it takes **9** days for **12** gardeners to landscape a new garden, how many days would it take **4** gardeners to complete the same job? _____ days

b) Rory and Carla together have **90** stamps. Derek and Rory together have **210** stamps. If there are **249** stamps in total how many stamps does each child have?

Rory: _____ Carla: _____ Derek: _____

Derek gives some of his stamps to Rory and Carla so they all have the same number of stamps.
i) How many does Derek give to Carla? _____ stamps
ii) How many does Derek give to Rory? _____ stamps

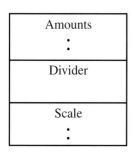

8) a) Timothy builds a model airplane from a scale plan. His airplane is **20cm** in length. The real airplane is **10** metres long. What is the scale on the plan? ____ : ____

b) A farmer walks around the perimeter of his land. He finds it measures **8.5km**. A plan of his land was drawn up to a scale of **1cm** to **50m**. What was the length of the perimeter on the map? _____ cm

9) a) Write the following scales in the form **1 : n**.

7mm : 98cm = ___ : ___   **25m : 2.5km** = ___ : ___

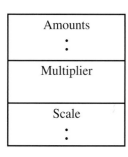

b) A map of England is drawn to a scale of **1 : 550,000**. What would a distance of **264** kilometres be in centimetres on the map?
_____ cm

10) a) A boy cycles up a steep hill on his mountain bike for **140** metres. The height of the hill is **80** metres. Write the gradient as a ratio ___ : ___ and expressed as **1 : n** ___ : ___

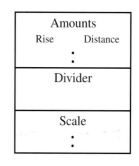

b) A cross country runner jogs down a slope for **75m**. If the gradient of the slope is **5%**, what is the rise? The rise is _____ m.

Score

11. Probability

Exercise 21: 11 Answer the following:

1) Write if the following events are certain, likely, possible, unlikely or impossible.

   a) You could buy the Crown Jewels. _____

   b) Working hard could make you a millionaire. _____

2) a) Does a die with some of its spots rubbed off have symmetry characteristics? Yes or no? _____

   b) If I draw a card from a complete set of **52** playing cards, will the outcome be 'fair' or 'unfair'? _____

3) a) If a 'fair' coin is tossed and it lands on tails, is this a mutually exclusive event? Yes or no? _____

   b) What is the set of all possible outcomes if a spinner with **5** sides is spun? The sides are labelled A to E.

   ____ ____ ____ ____ ____

4) a) Adam (**A**), Barry (**B**), Colin (**C**), Doris (**D**) and Eva (**E**) organise a table tennis tournament. They write their names on pieces of paper and place them in a bowl. To work out the order of play, they draw out two names each time and then replace them. This is repeated until all the possibilities are exhausted. List all the possible outcomes: ____ ____ ____

   ____ ____ ____ ____ ____ ____ ____

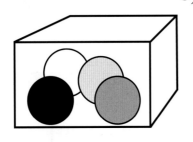

   b) A box contains four balls; black, dark grey, light grey and white. A ball is drawn out at random and replaced. The box is shaken and another ball is drawn out. This is one event. How many events would there be in total? _____

                                    ae

5) a) If two 'fair' dice are thown at once, what is the chance of achieving a score of **10**? A _____ chance.

   b) **255** raffle tickets are sold at a fair. Tickets are sold in blocks of **15** and no tickets are left over. Each person has a _____ chance of winning the raffle.

6) A jar is filled with coloured counters: **25** are red, **45** are green, **65** are yellow and **15** are blue. The jar is shaken. Work out the probability:

   a) of picking a red counter (write as a fraction). _____
   b) of not picking a blue counter (write as a %). _____%

7) a) There are **52** playing cards in a pack. In a game they are shuffled and dealt fairly. What is the chance the first card dealt will be a heart, club or spade? _____

   b) What is the probability that the first card will be a Jack or a Queen? _____

8) A two-way table shows whether the children in one class prefer cats or dogs as pets. What is the probability that:

Pets	Boys	Girls	Total
Cats	12	10	22
Dogs	6	4	10
Total	18	14	32

   a) a random boy prefers dogs?
   P(boy prefers dogs) = _____

   b) a random child prefers cats?
   P(child prefers cats) = _____

9) a) If two coins are tossed **60** times, how many times would you expect the coins to land on two heads? _____ times

   b) If one coin is tossed **40** times and it lands on tails **18** times, calculate the relative frequency. _____

10) Two dice are thrown until all the possible outcomes are exhausted. Draw a sample space diagram to find:

   a) P(score of 9) = _____   b) P(factors of 12) = _____

12. Lines and Angles

Exercise 21: 12 Answer the following:

1) a) Lines drawn together in this way are called _____ lines.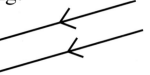

b) A graph is drawn with an **x-axis** and a **y-axis**. These lines would be _____ to each other.

2) a) What kind of angle is this?

A(n) _____ angle.

b) Is this angle acute, obtuse or reflex? _____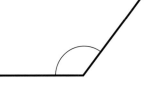

3) a) If two or more angles add together to make **180°**, the relationship between the angles is described as _____ .

b) What is the line/angle relationship between angle **a** and angle **b**?

_____

4) a) What type of angle is angle **a**?

A(n) _____ angle.

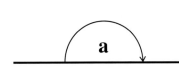

b) How many degrees are there in a $\frac{5}{8}$ turn? _____°

5) a) Angles **a**, **b** and **c** could be said to be in a _____ relationship.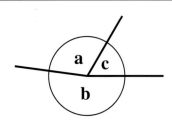

b) Angle **b** is a(n) _____ angle.

6) Find the missing angles:

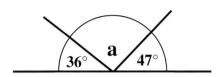 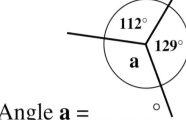

a) Angle **a** = _____ °   b) Angle **a** = _____ °

7) a) What is the missing angle as a fraction?

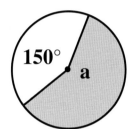

_____

b) Express **108°** as a fraction of **360°**.

_____

8) a) Write $\frac{7}{9}$ of a full rotation in degrees.

_____ °

b) What is the shaded part as a fraction?

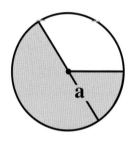

_____

9) a) June was heading in a north-easterly direction. She realised she had forgotten her keys, turned around and went back the way she came. In which direction would she now be heading? _____

b) Robert is walking south-west. He turns one right angle anticlockwise. On what bearing is he now walking? _____ °

North

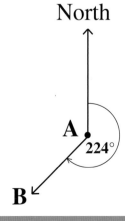

10) Calculate the following:
   a) Bearing **B** from **A**.

   _____ °

   b) Back bearing **A** from **B**.

   _____ °

Score

13. Time

Exercise 21: 13 Answer the following:

Score

1) a) How many months of the year have **30** days? ____ months

   b) How many days are there from the **2nd** of September to the **10th** of December? ____ days

2) a) What day of the week is the **23rd** of April (it is a leap year)?

   _____

January						
Su	M	Tu	W	Th	F	Sa
			1	2	3	4
5	6	7	8	9	10	11

   b) How many minutes and seconds are there in **229** seconds? ____ mins ____ secs

3) a) Convert $\frac{3}{5}$ of an hour into minutes. ____ mins

   b) What is **47** minutes in degrees? ____°

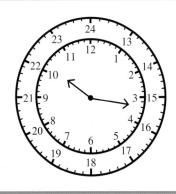

4) a) Write this time in 24-hour clock in the evening. ____ : ____

   b) Write the time in 12-hour clock in the morning. _____

5) a) A boy leaves for school on the bus at **7.09am**. This journey takes **9** minutes. He arrives at the station and waits for **14** minutes. He takes the train and travels for **49** minutes. His walk to school takes **17** minutes. What time does he arrive? _____ am

   b) How many hours and minutes are there between **11.33pm** and **6.51am**? _____ hrs _____ mins

6) a) Prianka revises for an examination for **2** hours and **40** minutes every day for **8** days. For how many hours and minutes does Prianka revise? ____ hrs ____ mins

b) A tutor works with **5** children for **1.5** hours each day for **4** days. If she divided up her time equally between the children, how many hours and minutes would she spend with each child individually? ____ hr(s) ____ mins

7) a) Holly is **5** times older than her niece. Her niece is **4** years and **7** months old. How old is Holly? ____ yrs ____ mths

b) Brenda's plane lands **27** minutes early. It should have arrived at **16:09** at Heathrow. Brenda's watch is **11** minutes slow. What time did Brenda's watch say when the plane landed? _____pm

8) a) It took John a different length of time to get to work each day. On Monday it took **1hr 55mins**, Tuesday **1hr 27mins**, Wednesday **2hrs 5mins**, Thursday **1hr 45mins** and Friday **2hrs 8mins**. What was the average length of time it took John to get to work that week? ____ hr(s) ____ mins

b) When it is **22:30** in London it is **07:30** in Japan. What time is it in London when it is **02:24** in Japan? _____

9) This is a table of bus journeys. Fill in the missing information on the table.

Distance	Time	Avg Speed
a) ____ miles	1hr 10mins	27mph
18 miles	b) ____mins	45mph
44 miles	55mins	c) ____mph

10) a) A cyclist rides at an average speed of **18mph** for **15** miles. How long did this take? _____ mins

b) The cyclist rides another **19** miles which takes **2** hours. Find his average speed for the whole journey. _____mph

14. Symmetry

Exercise 21: 14

Write the following for each shape:
a) Number of lines of symmetry.
b) The rotational order.

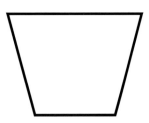

1) a) ___ line(s)
   b) R/O: ___

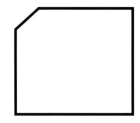

2) a) ___ line(s)
   b) R/O: ___

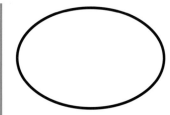

3) a) ___ line(s)
   b) R/O: ___

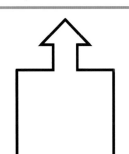

4) a) ___ line(s)
   b) R/O: ___

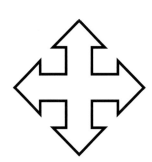

5) a) ___ line(s)
   b) R/O: ___

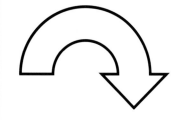

6) a) ___ line(s)
   b) R/O: ___

7) a) ___ line(s)
   b) R/O: ___

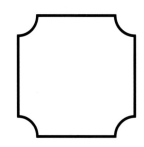

8) a) ___ line(s)
   b) R/O: ___

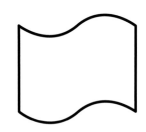

9) a) ___ line(s)
   b) R/O: ___

10) a) List the shapes that have no rotational symmetry.

   _____

   b) List the symmetrical shapes.

   _____

Score

15. Shapes

Exercise 21: 15 Answer the following:

1) a) Name this triangle. _____
   b) It has _____ line(s) of symmetry, _____ equal angles and a rotational order of _____ .

2) a) What four-sided shape has two parallel sides but no rotational symmetry? _____

   b) How many lines of symmetry does a parallelogram have? _____

3) a) This shape is called a _____ _____ and it has a rotational order of _____ .

   b) An ellipse has a rotational order of _____ and line symmetry of _____ .

4) a) Seven-sided shapes are called _____ .

   b) Decagons have _____ sides, hendecagons have _____ sides and dodecagons have _____ sides.

5) a) Write the names of these shaded parts of a circle.

   _____   _____   _____

   b) The interior angles of a triangle add up to _____° and the interior angles of a quadrilateral add up to _____°.

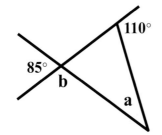

6) What size are angles **a** and **b**?
   a) Angle **a** is _____ degrees.
   b) Angle **b** is _____ degrees.

7) a) This shape is called either a _____
      or a _____ _____ _____ .

   b) It has ____ faces, ____ vertices and ____ edges.

8) a) There are two characteristics that identify a shape as
      a prism:
      Both ends are _____

      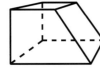 and _____ .

      b) Is this shape a prism? Yes or no? _____

9) a) Name these three-dimensional shapes:

 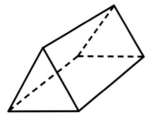  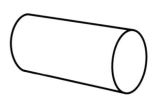

   _____   _____   _____   _____

   b) Which of these 3D shapes are prisms?

   _____

10) a) Which 3D shape is constructed from two square-based
       pyramids? _____

    b) This three-dimensional shape has ____ faces,
       ____ edges and ____ vertices.

16. Perimeter, Area and Volume

Exercise 21: 16 Answer the following:

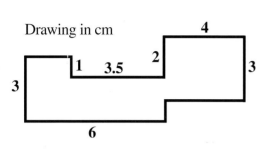

Drawing in cm

1) a) Calculate the perimeter of this shape. _____ cm

   b) The area of the shape is _____ cm².

2) a) A rectangle has a perimeter of **26cm** and a width of **3.5cm**. The area of the rectangle is _____ cm².

   b) The area of a square is **49m²**. The perimeter would measure _____ m.

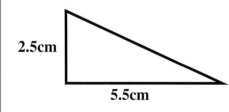

2.5cm

5.5cm

3) a) Find the area of this triangle. _____ cm² (to 2 d.p.)

   b) A triangle has a base of **200cm** and an area of **2m²**. What is the height of the triangle? _____ cm

4) a) What is the area of this parallelogram? _____ cm²

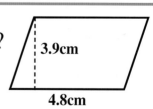

3.9cm

4.8cm

   b) If the area of a parallelogram is **78cm²** and its base is **13cm**, what is its height? _____ cm

5) a) The diameter of a circle is **8.5m**, so its circumference will be _____ m (to the nearest metre).

   b) If the circumference of a circle is **110mm**, what will the radius measure? _____ cm (to 1 d.p.)

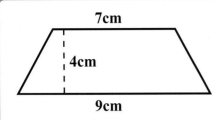

6) a) Find the area of this isosceles trapezium. _____ cm²

b) The area of a trapezium is **45cm²**. If the base is **8cm** and the top is **7cm**, what is its height? _____ cm

7) a) What is the surface area of this cuboid? _____ cm²

b) The volume of the cuboid is _____ cm³.

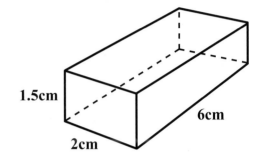

8) a) Convert **300cm²** to **m²**. _____ m²

b) How many hectares are there in **14km²**? _____ ha

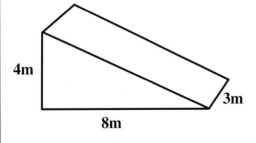

9) a) An access ramp for bicycles was built. What is the volume of the ramp? _____ m³

b) What is the volume of this drainage pipe to the nearest cubed metre? _____ m³

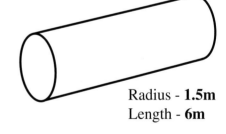

Radius - **1.5m**
Length - **6m**

10) a) Find the area of the tap washer to one decimal place. It has an outer radius of **1.6cm** and inner radius of **1.2cm**. _____ cm²

b) A water butt that holds **72** litres of water is **one third** full. How much would the water in the butt weigh? _____ kg

17. Geometry

Exercise 21: 17 Answer the following:

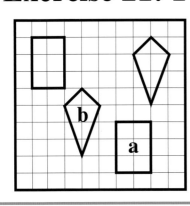

1) How have these shapes been translated?
   a) ____ squares up and ____ squares left.
   b) ____ squares right and ____ squares up.

2) Have these shapes been topologically transformed?

   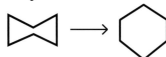

   a) Yes or no? ____   b) Yes or no? ____

3) a) Reflect shapes **x** and **y** across the mirror line of this grid.

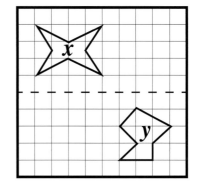

   b) Name shapes **x** and **y**:
      Shape **x** is a(n) _____
      _____ and shape **y** is
      a(n) _____ _____ .

4) Are these groups of shapes similar or congruent?

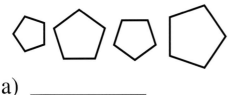

   a) _____   b) _____

5) a) Direct airplane **a** to the Hangar:
      F4, T/R, _____
      _____
      _____

   b) Direct airplane **b** to the Runway and Take-off:
      F3, T/L, _____
      _____
      _____

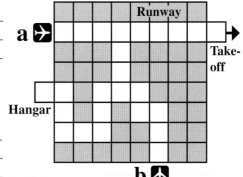

6) a) Will this heptagon tesselate? Yes or no? _____

b) Is this network transversable? Yes or no? _____

7) Plot the coordinates and join them up to make shapes.

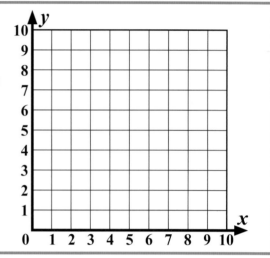

a) (**1, 5**) (**1, 7**) (**3, 9**) (**5, 7**) (**5, 5**) (**3, 3**)
   This shape is a(n)

   _____ .

b) (**6, 2**) (**6, 9**) (**9, 5**) (**7, 5**)
   (**7, 2**) (**8, 1**) (**7, 1**)
   This shape is a(n)

   _____ .

8) This is a village plan.

a) Give grid references for the:
   Store: _____ Bank: _____
   Post Office: _____

b) What can be found at:
   B9: _____
   G7: _____
   J6: _____

9) Plot the points and join them up:

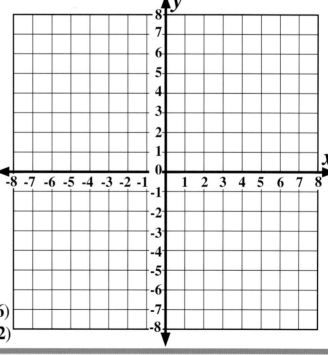

a) (**-6, 7**) (**-1, 7**) (**-6, 4**) (**2, 4**)
b) This shape is a(n)

   _____ .

10) Plot the points and join them up:

a) (**-7, 1**) (**-6, 3**) (**-4, 3**) (**-3, 1**)
   (**-3, -2**) (**-4, -4**) (**-6, -4**) (**-7, -2**)

b) This shape is a(n)

   _____ .

c) (**3, 6**) (**4, 2**) (**8, 1**) (**5, -1**) (**6, -6**)
   (**3, -3**) (**0, -6**) (**1, -1**) (**-2, 1**) (**2, 2**)

18. Tables, Charts, Graphs and Diagrams

Exercise 21: 18 Answer the following:

Score

1) This table records the votes of a primary class' election for a new class captain.
   a) How many children did not vote for Jane or Milly? _____
   b) How many votes were cast altogether? _____

Name	Votes
Paul	17
Jane	6
Milly	7
Abstain	2

2) A distance table shows distances in miles between five villages.

Tipton				
15	Midley			
17	18	Ashton		
35	37	39	Rutley	
57	72	61	75	Tarrow

   a) How far is it from Ashton to Tarrow and back? _____ miles
   b) A nurse lives in Midley and visits one village per day during one working week. How far does she travel? _____ miles

3) This is a survey of lottery wins in Denton village over a 10-year period.

   Villagers never achieved more than **12** wins during the period.

   a) Using a class interval of **3** wins, complete the table.
   2, 6, 3, 9, 4, 3, 2, 1, 3, 8, 12, 6, 3, 2, 7, 11, 5, 7, 8, 3
   4, 7, 4, 5, 6, 1, 2, 4, 3, 6, 9, 12, 6, 8, 1, 5, 10, 5, 2, 1
   b) What was the frequency of under **10** wins? Frequency of _____ .

Wins	Tally	Fr
1-3	IIII IIII IIII	15

4) The eye colour of four primary classes was surveyed and the results were partially recorded on a pie chart.
   a) How many children had hazel eyes? _____
   b) How many children were surveyed altogether? _____

Amber, Brown, Hazel, Green, Grey, 16 had blue eyes

5) A supermarket checkout records how many full trolleys were processed by one shop assistant in a week.

Monday	🛒 🛒 🛒 🛒 🛒 🛒 🛒
Tuesday	🛒 🛒 🛒 🛒 🛒
Wednesday	🛒 🛒 🛒 🛒 🛒 🛒 🛒
Thursday	🛒 🛒 🛒 🛒 🛒 🛒 🛒 🛒
Friday	🛒 🛒 🛒 🛒 🛒 🛒 🛒 🛒 🛒 🛒 🛒

a) How many more trolleys were processed on Friday than Monday? _____

b) Which day was the least busy for the shop assistant? _____

c) How many trolleys were processed over the whole week? _____

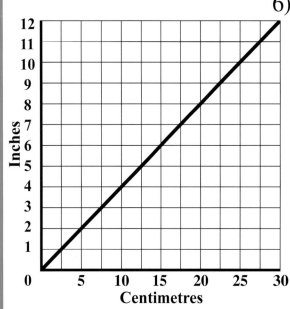

6) This conversion graph shows approximate conversions for inches and centimetres.

a) **30cm ≈** _____ inches

b) **5 inches ≈** _____ cm

c) **22.5cm ≈** _____ inches

d) Approximately what is **3** feet in cm? _____ cm

e) A boy is **165cm** tall. What would this approximately be in feet? _____ ft _____ ins

7) A train travels **450** miles. Find the speed for stages:

a) **A** to **B** = _____ mph

b) **D** to **E** = _____ mph

c) **C** to **D** = _____ mph

d) What was the total distance travelled at **12.5mph**? _____ miles

e) Calculate the average speed for the whole journey. _____ mph

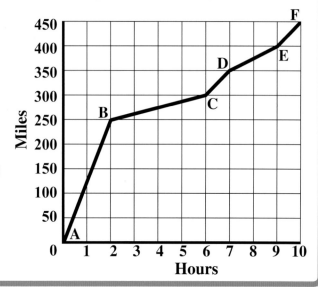

8) The end of year overall examination results for a school's two year 6 classes were compared (class 1 and class 2).

Class 1			Class 2		
Grade	Mark (%)	Fr	Grade	Mark (%)	Fr
A	81-100	2	A	81-100	5
B	61-80	7	B	61-80	9
C	41-60	14	C	41-60	8
D	21-40	4	D	21-40	7
E	1-20	3	E	1-20	1

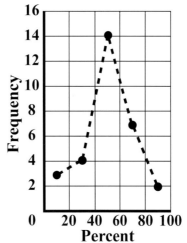

a) Plot the points for class 2 and join them up.
b) Which class achieved the most A-C grades? _____
c) Overall how many children achieved an A grade? _____
d) Which class achieved the most D-E grades? _____
e) According to the graph, which class did better overall? _____

Key
Class 1
- - - - -
Class 2

9) The bar chart shows the shoe sizes of a class of children.

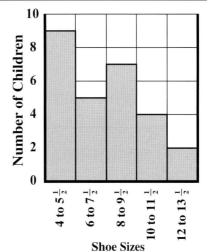

a) How many children have a shoe size of at least **6** but less than **10**? _____ children
b) There are **13** children with a shoe size that is less than **8**. True or false? _____
c) How many children have a shoe size that is greater than **8**? _____ children
d) How many children were there in the class? _____ children

10) Complete the sets and intersections of the sets made from the **7×**, **8×** and **12×** tables up to **12** on this Venn diagram.

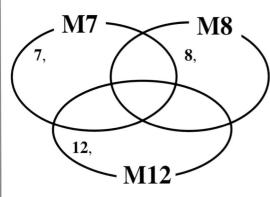

Here is the **M7** set to get you started:
Set **M7** = {7, 14, 21, 28, 35, 42, 49, 56, 63, 70, 77, 84}

Answer the following questions:
a) **M7** ∩ **M8** = {_____}
b) **M7** ∩ **M12** = {_____}
c) **M8** ∩ **M12** = {_____}
d) **M7** ∩ **M8** ∩ **M12** = {_____}
e) **M8** cup **M12** = {_____

_____}

19. Algebra

Exercise 21: 19   Answer the following: Score

1) a) $-3 + -7 =$ _____   b) $+21 \div -7 =$ _____

2) a) $-3(-4 + 2) - 9 =$ _____   b) _____ $\rightarrow$ $\boxed{\times 5 \ +4}$ $\rightarrow$ **69**

   c) $(4^3 + 2^4) - (5 - 2)^2 =$ _____

3) If $x = 7$, $y = -2$ and $z = 5$

   a) $4x + 3z - 4y =$ _____   b) $3(x + 2z + 2y) =$ _____

4) a) What is the algebraic rule for this sequence?

   5, 8, 11, 14, 17 _____

   What is the: b) **10th** term? _____   c) **23rd** term? _____

5) The formula for triangular numbers is $n(n + 1) \div 2$
    Find the following triangular numbers:

   a) **8th** _____   b) **15th** _____   c) **60th** _____

   d) **Seven** tennis players take part in a club tournament.
       They all play each other once. How many matches
       will there be in total? _____ matches

6) a) Rikhil cycles x miles to school for a week. He cycles
      back and forth each day. He also cycles to school on
      Saturday to play football but his father collects him
      because he is injured during the match. How many
      miles does Rikhil cycle over the week? _____ miles

   b) x is $\dfrac{1}{3}$ of y If y is **12**, what is x? _____

7) a) $5y - 3 = 22$ b) $4(x - 2) = 3(4x - 2)$

$y =$ _____ $x =$ _____

c) $4(x + 4) = 10x - 8$ d) $\dfrac{x}{12} + 9 = 3$

$x =$ _____ $x =$ _____

8) **48** less than **4** times a number is equal to the number. If x is the number, find the number.

a) The equation is _____   b) $x =$ _____

9) a) Draw lines for these two simultaneous equations. Use the cover and draw method on: $3x + 6y = 18$

Fill in the table of values for: $y = 3x - 4$

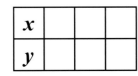

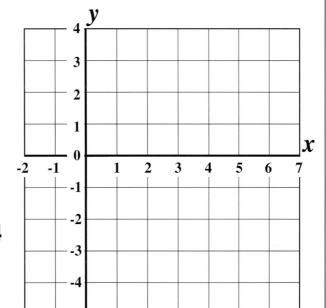

b) Where do the lines meet? $x =$ _____ $y =$ _____

10) a) Solve these simultaneous equations by using the algebraic method:

$2x + y = 7$ $3x - y = 8$ $x =$ _____ $y =$ _____

b) The equations $5x + 2y = 48$ and $3x + 2y = 32$ stand for the money collected for a school trip during two lessons. If £x represents the cost for teachers and £y represents the cost for pupils, what is the cost for each teacher? £ _____

20. Mathematical Instruments

Exercise 21: 20   Answer the following:

1) Using a set square, draw the following:

a) A parallelogram with two **60°**   b) A scalene triangle has another side
   angles. The short side is **1.5cm**.   of **2.5cm** and one angle of **30°**.

Use a calculator for the following questions:

2) a) $96 \times 4 \div 3 \times 6 =$ _____   b) $38 \times {}^-22 \div 4 \times {}^-2 =$ _____

---

3) a) ${}^-3(5 - {}^-2) \times 10 =$ _____   b) $51 \div {}^-3 + 2({}^-7 \times 9) =$ _____

Use the calculator memory for these two questions:

4) a) Calculate **121 × 5**, then subtract **127 + 279**, then
   subtract **16 × 8** and then add **4200 ÷ 84**. _____

  b) Add **17 × 13** to **294 ÷ 14**, then subtract **38 × 4** and then
   subtract **117 − 49**. _____

---

5) a) $5.4 - 3 \times 7 + 8.9 =$ _____   b) $48 \times 2.8 \div 1.4 \times 6 =$ _____

Fix the calculator at 2 decimal places:

6) a) $3.69 \div 5 \times 78.3 =$ _____   b) $29.3 - 7.72 \times 8.7 =$ _____

---

7) a) $6\frac{3}{8} \times \frac{5}{6} \div 2\frac{1}{4} = \underline{}$ b) $\frac{5}{8} \times 3\frac{1}{3} - 1\frac{3}{5} = \underline{}$

---

8) a) **27%** of $18\frac{3}{4} = \underline{}$ b) **17** as a % of **136** = _____ %

---

9) a) $16^3 \div 32 - 6^3 =$ _____   b) $14^2 - 144 + \sqrt[3]{512} =$ _____

---

10) a) Find the area of a circle with a radius of **1.2m**. ___ m²
   b) Find the circumference of the circle. _____ m (to 2 d.p.)

Answers

Chapter Twenty
Mathematical Instruments
Exercise 20: 1

1) 25mm
2) 61mm
3) 47mm
4) 16mm
5) 9cm 9mm
6) 3cm 1mm
7) 12.4cm
8) 15cm
9) 11.8cm
10) 17.3cm

Exercise 20: 2

1)
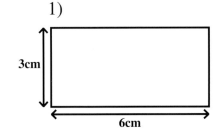

2)
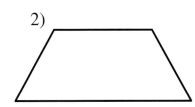

3)
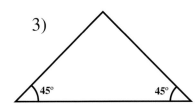

4)
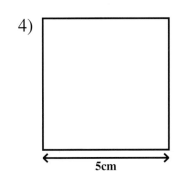

5)
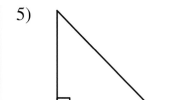

6)
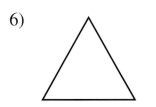

7)
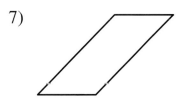

8)
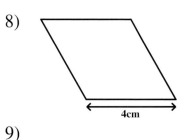

9)
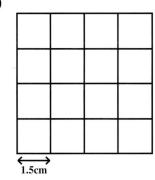

10)
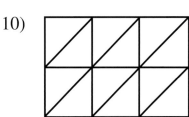

Exercise 20: 3

1) a) Range: 125°-145°
   Actual: 135 degrees
   b) Range: 50°-70°
   Actual: 60 degrees

2) a) Range: 190°-210°
   Actual: 200 degrees
   b) Range: 150°-170°
   Actual: 160 degrees

3) 77 degrees
4) 120 degrees
5) 150 degrees
6) 240 degrees
7) A is 45 degrees
   B is 75 degrees
   C is 60 degrees

8)
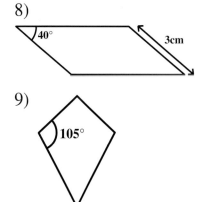

9)
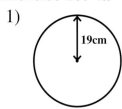

10) A is 110 degrees
    B is 70 degrees

Exercise 20: 4a

1)
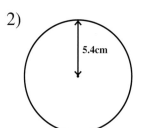

2)

3)
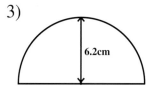

Answers

4)

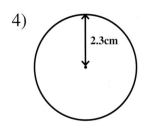

Exercise 20: 4b

5)

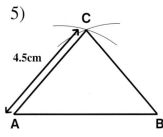

6)

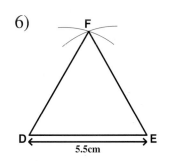

7)

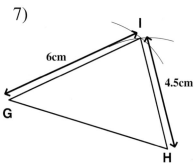

8)

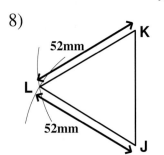

9)

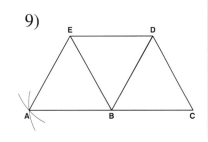

10)

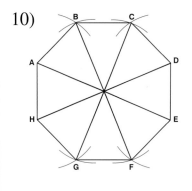

Exercise 20: 5a

1)

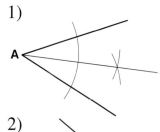

2)

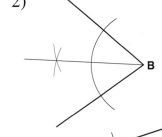

3)

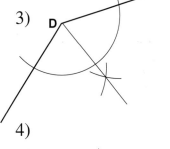

4)

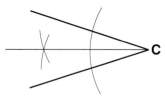

5) Rectangle

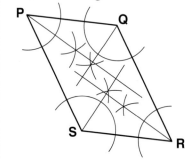

6) Yes

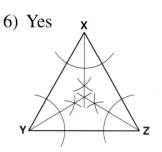

Exercise 20: 5b

7)

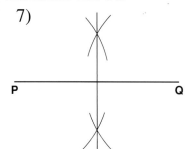

8)

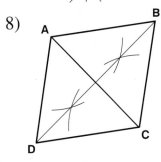

9)

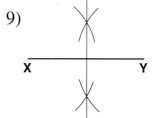

10)

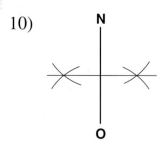

Exercise 20: 6a

1) 9	2) 12
3) 47	4) 1,190
5) 107	

Exercise 20: 6b

6) -37	7) 4
8) 253	9) 637
10) -2,824	

Exercise 20: 7a
1) 504   2) -148
3) -396   4) 1,170
5) 5,052

Exercise 20: 7b
6) 4,945   7) 953
8) 221   9) 223
10) 2,398

Exercise 20: 8
1) 6   2) 459
3) 248   4) 3,026
5) 1,136   6) 4,594
7) 55,833   8) 62,584
9) 2,261   10) 2,195

Exercise 20: 9
1) 9   2) 12
3) 1,190   4) 30.8
5) 6.3   6) 33.68
7) 40.86   8) 422.5
9) 293.04   10) 112.31

Exercise 20: 10
1) 39.5   2) 15.4
3) 31.5   4) 664.7
5) 31.63   6) 120.65
7) 506.26   8) 58.18
9) 88.238   10) 27.106

Exercise 20: 11a
1) $^3/_4$ 2) $^4/_7$ 3) $^{13}/_2$
4) $^{50}/_9$ 5) $^{175}/_{12}$

Exercise 20: 11b
6) 2 ⌐3   7) 5 ⌐ 8
8) 4 ⌐ 2 ⌐ 7
9) 3 ⌐ 7 ⌐ 10
10) 11 ⌐ 3 ⌐ 5

Exercise 20: 12
1) $^7/_{12}$ 2) $3^{17}/_{63}$

3) $2^1/_{12}$ 4) $1^1/_4$
5) $^{29}/_{60}$ 6) $^1/_4$
7) $3^1/_{12}$ 8) $1^9/_{10}$
9) $17^{13}/_{35}$ 10) $84^7/_{12}$

Exercise 20: 13a
1) £3.06   2) 19.43
3) 1.61   4) 69p
5) 468kg

Exercise 20: 13b
6) 85%   7) 22.5%
8) 5%   9) 62.5%
10) 65%

Exercise 20: 14a
1) 277   2) 6,423
3) 229.75   4) 73.2
5) 34.2

Exercise 20: 14b
6) 2,237   7) 5,103
8) 84   9) 9.34
10) 12,288

Exercise 20: 15
1) 53.41cm
2) 8m² 3) 19.635cm²
4) 15.708cm 5) 7.5m
6) 16.6m²   7) 16.7m
8) 88.36cm²
9) 23.56cm
10) 618.5cm³

Chapter Twenty One
Revision
Exercise 21: 1
1) a) 13,093
   b) Four hundred and
      twenty-three
      thousand, two
      hundred and
      ninety-six

2) a) 32,077 b) 6, 8, 9, 2
3) a) 9,831   b) 5,169
4) a) 55,692 b) 24,702
5) a) 28,900 b) 439
6) a) 25,632 b) 28,000
7) a) 52   b) 27 r. 4
8) a) 18   b) 306   c) 3
9) a) 10   b) 19
10) a) 633   b) 226

Exercise 21: 2
1) a) 6   b) 40
2) a) 361   b) 13
3) a) 4,096 b) 5
4) a) 49
   b) 6, 8, 9, 10, 12, 14,
      15, 16, 18
5) a) 78   b) 4, 2
6) a) 37   b) 40
7) a) 6 and -8 b) 0
8) a) 15, 18, 20
   b) 1, 2, 3, 4, 6, 8, 12,
      16, 24, 48
9) a) 13   b) 126
10) a) 27 days b) 60 bags

Exercise 21: 3
1) a) 9 thousandths
   b) 5 units and 29
      hundredths
2) a) -57.4
   b) 1.009 1.09 1.9
3) a) 4.87   b) 0.9
4) a) C   b) >
5) a) 94.332 b) 19.926
6) a) 14.06   b) 100
7) a) 0.4   b) 4.93
8) a) × 0.01 b) 0.0136
9) a) 0.57 × 100 b) 5.5
10) a) 0.07 b) 7.001

Answers

Exercise 21: 4

1) a) $^{12}/_{19}$ b) 48
2) a) $^{41}/_7$ b) $6^4/_5$
3) a) $6^{17}/_{45}$ b) $1^4/_9$
4) a) $17^1/_3$ b) $2^{14}/_{15}$
5) a) 200 b) 245
6) a) $3^6/_{25}$ b) 0.86
7) a) $^5/_6, {}^6/_7, {}^7/_8, {}^8/_9$
   b) 0.45, $^3/_7, {}^2/_5$, 0.39
8) a) $6^2/_5$ b) $1^{19}/_{20}$
9) a) 72 b) 77
10) a) $^3/_{50}$ b) $^1/_5$
    c) $^3/_{10}$ d) 0.08
    e) 0.16 f) 0.34

Exercise 21: 5

1) a) 459p b) £0.87
2) a) £11.69 b) 768p
3) a) £82.88 b) £6.22
4) a) £2.46 b) 1,344p
5) a) £4.08 b) £12.75
6) a) £23.12 b) £59.50
7) a) £780 b) £1,950
8) a) 65p b) $140
9) a) £324.50 b) £235.10
10) a) £1.64 b) £1.50

Exercise 21: 6

1) a) 2,500g b) 15cℓ
2) a) 4km 3,000cm
   b) 35mℓ
3) a) 0.036km
   b) 74ℓ 630mℓ
4) a) 479cm
   b) 3.427kg
5) a) 5km 260m
   b) 4,510g
6) a) 0.096ℓ
   b) 0.426m
7) a) 6.062ℓ b) 27.5km
8) a) 10ft b) 20km

9) a) 5kg b) 1,000ℓ
10) a) 5.2cm b) 0.052m

Exercise 21: 7

1) a) 5 b) 7 c) 7
2) a) 26° b) 9°
3) a) 6 b) 637
4) a) £9.00 b) 1.7 litres
5) a) 62 days b) 15 days
6) a) 912cm b) £560
7) a) £2.35 b) £2.46
8) a) 512 b) 14.3
9) a) 11 hours b) 75 hours
10) a) 118cm b) 1.26m

Exercise 21: 8

1) a) 100111_2 b) 26_{10}
2) a) 101010_2 b) 11011_2
3) a) 111001_2
   b) 1010_2 r. 10_2
4) a) 2001_3 b) 77_{10}
5) a) 2122_3 b) 1022_3
6) a) 11002_3 b) 1122_3
7) a) 2102_5 b) 33_{10}
8) a) 1104_5 b) 133_5
9) a) 11044_5 b) 434_5
10) a) Base 4 b) Base 6

Exercise 21: 9

1) a) $^{14}/_{25}$ b) 62.5%
2) a) £1.21 b) 0.143km
3) a) £598 b) 11,400g
4) a) 400 b) £6.00
5) a) 65% b) 62.5%
6) a) 350% b) 18%
7) a) 45% b) £487.50
8) a) 1.22 b) 9%
9) a) 0.3, $^7/_{24}$, 26%, $^6/_{25}$, 0.23
   b) 0.04, $^1/_{20}$, 5.44%,
      6.1%, $^2/_{27}$
10) a) 24% and 60%

   b) 12.5% and 40%

Exercise 21: 10

1) a) 5 : 6 b) 40%
2) a) 3 : 10, $^3/_{13} : {}^{10}/_{13}$
   b) 5 : 4, $^5/_9 : {}^4/_9$
3) a) 3 : 1, 75% : 25%
   b) 1 : 4 : 6
4) a) 17 : 1 b) 1 : 10
5) a) 39 : 65 b) 27 boys
6) a) 3 cakes
   b) Paul: 210
      Rumina: 42
      Lesley: 14
7) a) 27 days
   b) Rory: 51
      Carla: 39
      Derek: 159
      i) 44
      ii) 32
8) a) 1 : 50
   b) 170cm
9) a) 1 : 140 and 1 : 100
   b) 48cm
10) a) 4 : 7 and 1 : 1.75
    b) 3.75m

Exercise 21: 11

1) a) Impossible
   b) Possible
2) a) No b) Fair
3) a) Yes
   b) A, B, C, D, E
4) a) AB, AC, AD, AE,
      BC, BD, BE, CD,
      CE, DE
   b) 16
5) a) 1 in 12
   b) 1 in 17
6) a) $^1/_6$ b) 90%
7) a) 3 in 4

Answers

b) 2 in 13

8) a) $^1/_3$ b) $^{11}/_{16}$

9) a) 20

   b) 0.45

10) a) $^1/_9$ b) $^1/_3$

Exercise 21: 12

1) a) parallel

   b) perpendicular

2) a) right

   b) Obtuse

3) a) supplementary

   b) Complementary

4) a) straight line

   b) 225°

5) a) conjugate

   b) reflex

6) a) 97°   b) 119°

7) a) $^7/_{12}$ b) $^3/_{10}$

8) a) 280°   b) $^2/_3$

9) a) South-west

   b) 135°

10) a) 224°   b) 44°

Exercise 21: 13

1) a) 4

   b) 99

2) a) Thursday

   b) 3mins 49secs

3) a) 36mins b) 282°

4) a) 22:17

   b) 10.17am

5) a) 8.38am

   b) 16hrs 42mins

6) a) 21hrs 20mins

   b) 1hr 12mins

7) a) 22yrs 11mths

   b) 3.31pm

8) a) 1hr 52mins

   b) 17:24

9) a) 31.5 miles

   b) 24mins c) 48mph

10) a) 50mins b) 12mph

Exercise 21: 14

1) a) 1 line   b) R/O: 1

2) a) 0 lines   b) R/O: 1

3) a) 2 lines   b) R/O: 2

4) a) 1 line   b) R/O: 1

5) a) 4 lines   b) R/O: 4

6) a) 0 lines   b) R/O: 1

7) a) 2 lines   b) R/O: 2

8) a) 4 lines   b) R/O: 4

9) a) 0 lines   b) R/O: 2

10) a) Shapes 1, 2, 4, 6

    b) Shapes 1, 3, 4, 5, 7, 8

Exercise 21: 15

1) a) Isosceles

   b) 1; 2; 1

2) a) Trapezium b) None

3) a) regular nonagon; 9

   b) 2; 2

4) a) heptagons

   b) 10; 11; 12

5) a) Segment; Sector;
      Quadrant

   b) 180°; 360°

6) a) 25

   b) 95

7) a) tetrahedron or
      triangular based
      pyramid

   b) 4; 4; 6

8) a) Both ends are the
      same shape and
      size and parallel
      to each other.

   b) Yes

9) a) Cone; Triangular
      Prism; Sphere;
      Cylinder

   b) Triangular Prism
      and Cylinder

10) a) Octahedron

    b) 8; 12; 6

Exercise 21: 16

1) a) 30cm   b) 26.5cm²

2) a) 33.25cm² b) 28m

3) a) 6.88cm²   b) 200cm

4) a) 18.72cm² b) 6cm

5) a) 27m   b) 17.5cm

6) a) 32cm²   b) 6cm

7) a) 48cm²   b) 18cm³

8) a) 0.03m²   b) 1,400ha

9) a) 48m³   b) 42m³

10) a) 3.5cm²   b) 24kg

Exercise 21: 17

1) a) 5; 5

   b) 4; 3

2) a) No b) Yes

3) a)

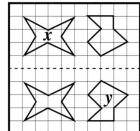

   b) irregular octagon;
      irregular heptagon

4) a) Similar

   b) Congruent

5) a) **F4, T/R**, F3, T/R, F1,
      T/L, F2, T/R, F2,
      T/R, F2, T/L, F1

   b) **F3, T/L**, F1, T/R, F1,
      T/L, F1, T/R, F3,
      T/R, F5

Answers

6) a) No   b) Yes

7)

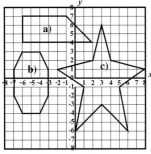

   a) irregular hexagon
   b) irregular heptagon

8) a) Store: H10
     Bank: F3
     Post Office: G1
   b) B9: Church
     G7: Coppice Sch.
     J6: Sports Hall

9-10)

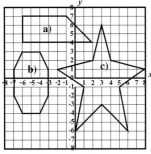

9) a) See shape a)
   b) trapezium
10) a) See shape b)
    b) octagon
    c) See shape c)

Exercise 21: 18

1) a) 19   b) 32
2) a) 122
   b) 284
3) a)

Wins	Tally	Fr
1-3	ＷＨＴ ＷＨＴ ＷＨＴ	15
4-6	ＷＨＴ ＷＨＴ III	13
7-9	ＷＨＴ III	8
10-12	IIII	4

   b) 36
4) a) 12
   b) 96

5) a) 40
   b) Tuesday
   c) 360
6) a) 12 inches b) 12.5cm
   c) 9 inches d) 90cm
   e) 5ft 6ins
7) a) 125mph b) 25mph
   c) 25mph   d) 50 miles
   e) 45mph
8) a)

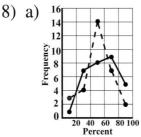

   b) Class 1 c) 7
   d) Class 2 e) Class 2
9) a) 12
   b) False
   c) 13
   d) 27
10) a) 56, 72   b) 72, 84
   c) 24, 36, 48, 72, 96
   d) 72
   e) 8, 12, 16, 24, 32,
      36, 40, 48, 60, 64,
      72, 80, 88, 96, 108,
      120, 132, 144

Exercise 21: 19

1) a) -10   b) -3
2) a) -3   b) 13   c) 71
3) a) 51   b) 39
4) a) $3x + 2$
   b) 32   c) 71
5) a) 36   b) 120
   c) 1,830 d) 21
6) a) $11x$ b) $x = 4$
7) a) $y = 5$ b) $x = -\frac{1}{4}$
   c) $x = 4$ d) $x = -72$

8) a) $4x - 48 = x$
   b) $x = 16$
9) a)

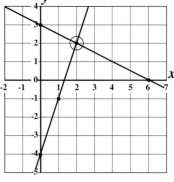

   b) $x = 2; y = 2$
10) a) $x = 3; y = 1$
    b) £8

$y = 3x - 4$

x	0	1	2
y	-4	-1	2

Exercise 21: 20

1) a)

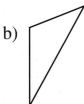

   b)

2) a) 768   b) 418
3) a) -210   b) -143
4) a) 121   b) 22
5) a) -6.7   b) 576
6) a) 57.79   b) -37.86
7) a) $2^{13}/_{36}$ b) $^{29}/_{60}$
8) a) $5^{1}/_{16}$ b) 12.5%
9) a) -88   b) 60
10) a) 4.52m² b) 7.54m

PROGRESS CHARTS

20. MATHEMATICAL INSTRUMENTS

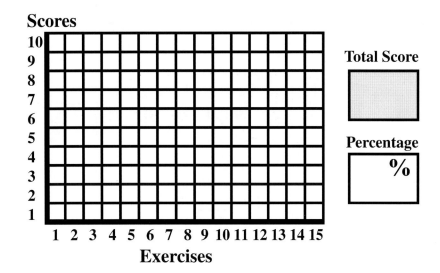

Total Score

Percentage %

21. REVISION

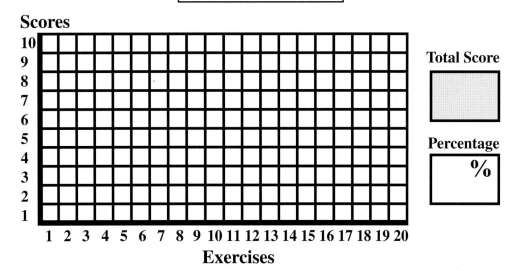

Total Score

Percentage %

Shade in your score for each exercise on the graphs. Add up for your total score.

For the average add up % and divide by 2

Overall Percentage

%

CERTIFICATE OF

ACHIEVEMENT

This certifies

_____

has successfully completed

11+ Maths
Year 5–7
WORKBOOK **7**

Overall percentage
score achieved

%

Comment _____

_____

Signed _____
(teacher/parent/guardian)

Date _____